Math in Focus®

Singapore Math

by Marshall Cavendish

Assessments

Author

Chelvi Ramakrishnan

Marshall Cavendish
Education

US Distributor

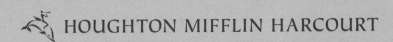
HOUGHTON MIFFLIN HARCOURT

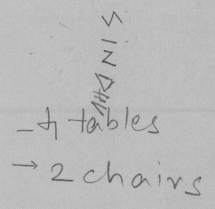

COMMON CORE

© 2013 Marshall Cavendish International (Singapore) Private Limited

Published by Marshall Cavendish Education
An imprint of Marshall Cavendish International (Singapore) Private Limited
Times Centre, 1 New Industrial Road, Singapore 536196
Customer Service Hotline: (65) 6411 0820
E-mail: tmesales@sg.marshallcavendish.com
Website: www.marshallcavendish.com/education

Distributed by
Houghton Mifflin Harcourt
222 Berkeley Street
Boston, MA 02116
Tel: 617-351-5000
Website: www.hmheducation.com/mathinfocus

First published 2013

Marshall Cavendish and *Math in Focus* are registered trademarks of Times Publishing Limited.

Math in Focus® Assessments 5
ISBN 978-0-547-87517-0

Printed in Singapore

2 3 4 5 6 7 8   1897   18 17 16 15 14 13
4500356445   A B C D E

Contents

iii

Introducing

Math in Focus®

Assessments

Assessments 5 is written to complement *Math in Focus®: Singapore Math by Marshall Cavendish* Grade 5.

Assessments 5 provides both a pretest and a chapter test for each chapter of the Student Books, as well as two Benchmark Assessments, a Mid-Year Test, and an End-of-Year Test. Assessments items for the Common Core Focus Lessons are also included. These items are to be used in conjunction with the chapter tests when applicable. Chapter tests are in test-prep format with a multiple-choice section and an open response section to help students become familiar and comfortable with formal assessment situations. Word problems and non-routine problems included throughout the tests provide important problem-solving practice.

BLANK

PRE-TEST 1

Whole Numbers

Vocabulary

Fill in the blanks.
Use the words in the box.

1. Each digit in a number has a _____ that is determined by its position or place in the number.

2. To _____ two numbers, decide whether one number is greater than, less than, or equal to the other number.

3. When _____ a number to the nearest hundred, check the digit in the tens place.

4. _____ uses the value of the leading digits to estimate sums and differences.

> rounding
>
> compare
>
> value
>
> front-end estimation

Concepts and Skills

Write your answer in the space given.

5. Write 15,732 in word form.

_____

6. Write 6 ten thousands in standard form.

_____

Find the value of the digit 4 in each number.

7.   **a.**   841,679 _____   **b.**   427,153 _____

Complete. Express each number in expanded form.

8.   **a.**   76,480 = 70, 000 + _____ + 400 + _____

      b.   620,315 = _____ + _____ + 300 + 10 + 5

Compare the numbers. Fill each ◯ with < or >.

9.   **a.**   76,200 ◯ 67,900

      b.   2,435,932 ◯ 2,805,743

Order the numbers from greatest to least.

10.   355,410   374,875   374,248

_____

Round each number to the nearest hundred.

11.   **a.**   37,923 _____   **b.**   56,379 _____

Estimate the sum or difference by rounding each number to the nearest thousand.

12. $4{,}182 + 6{,}893$

13. $9{,}731 - 2{,}890$

Estimate each sum or difference by using front-end estimation.

14. $562 + 814$

15. $937 - 486$

Estimate each product or quotient.

16. $2{,}742 \times 7$

17. $6{,}502 \div 9$

Problem Solving

Solve. Show your work.

18. Ms. Carlson has $7,145. Ms. Lee has $3,799.

  a. Who has more money?

  b. Estimate the total amount of money they have.

19. The length of a rectangular field is 315 feet. The width is 175 feet. Use front-end estimation to find the area of the rectangular field.

Whole Numbers

25

Suggested Time: 30 min

Multiple Choice (5 × 2 points = 10 points)

Fill in the circle next to the correct answer.

1. Which of these is the word form for 215,078?

(A) two hundred fifteen seventy-eight

(B) two hundred fifteen thousand

(C) two hundred fifteen thousand, seventy-eight

(D) two hundred thousand fifteen and seventy-eight

2. What is the value of 6 in 563,209?

(A) 600,000   (B) 60,000   (C) 600   (D) 6

3. Which of these is the least?

(A) 1,000,000   (B) 999,000   (C) 789,987   (D) 99,999

4. Which of these is 3,000 more than 568,210?

(A) 868,210   (B) 598,210   (C) 571,210   (D) 568,510

5. Estimate 5,215 + 2,783 by rounding each number to the nearest thousand.

(A) 6,000   (B) 7,000   (C) 8,000   (D) 9,000

Short Answer   (5 × 2 points = 10 points)

Write your answer in the space given.

6.   **a.**   Write 6,326,508 in word form.

_____

b.   Complete to express 4,781,020 in expanded form.

4,781,020 = _____ + 700,000 + 80,000 + 1,000 +

_____

Write >, <, or = in each ◯.

7.   **a.**   354,819 ◯ 354,981   **b.**   1,782,356 ◯ 928,339

Estimate each sum or difference by using front-end estimation with adjustment.

8.   2,691 + 8,173 + 4,724   **9.**   7,685 − 3,768

Find the rule. Then complete the number pattern.

10.   2,937,045   3,437,145   _____   4,437,345   _____

Rule: _____

Extended Response   (Question 11: 2 points, Question 12: 3 points)

Solve. Show your work.

11.   There are 9 passengers in each mini-bus. There are 6,157 mini-buses. Estimate the total number of passengers.

12.   Mr. James has 8 crates of mangoes. There are 3,548 mangoes in total. Estimate the number of mangoes in each crate.

Whole Number Multiplication and Division

Vocabulary

Fill in the blanks.
Use the words in the box.

1. The _____ of 3,672 is
   3,000 + 600 + 70 + 2.

2. Quotients can be estimated by using

   related _____.

3. The _____ of two numbers can be
   estimated by rounding.

4. A _____ can be used to show operations.

5. 3,642 rounded to the _____ is 4,000.

| nearest 1,000 |
| bar model |
| product |
| multiplication facts |
| expanded form |

Concepts and Skills

Write your answer in the space given.

6. Write 8,238,615 in word form and expanded form.

   a. Word form: _____

   b. Expanded form: _____

Find each missing symbol or number.

7.

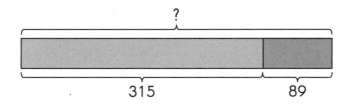

? = _____

8.

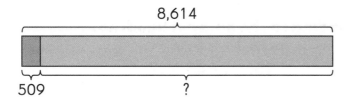

? = _____

9.

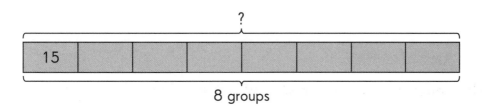

? = _____

10.

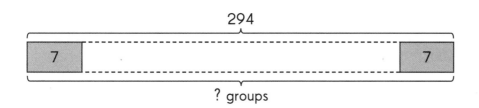

? = _____

11.

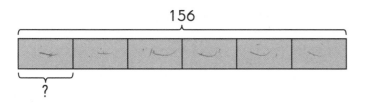

? = _____

Round each number to the nearest thousand.

12. 7,593   **13.** 81,764

Estimate each product by rounding to the nearest hundred.

14. 372 × 9   **15.** 845 × 7

Estimate each product by using front-end estimation.

16. 972 × 5   **17.** 271 × 8

Estimate each quotient by using related multiplication facts.

18. 372 ÷ 4   **19.** 197 ÷ 6

Problem Solving

Solve. Show your work.

20. Mr. Sims has 198 oranges. He packs them into 5 crates. Use rounding to estimate the number of oranges in each crate.

21. Pauline has 502 beads. There are 185 red beads.
The rest are green beads. How many green beads are there?
Draw a model to help you.

Solve. Show your work.

22.   Hector has 495 stamps. He wants to put 9 stamps into an envelope. How many envelopes will Hector need to put all his stamps?

Whole Number Multiplication and Division

25
Suggested Time:
30 min

Multiple Choice   (5 × 2 points = 10 points)

Fill in the circle next to the correct answer.

1.   Multiply 65 by 80.

(A) 520   (B) 5,200   (C) 52,000   (D) 52

2.   Which of these is a reasonable answer for 3,652 × 39?

(A) 86,428   (B) 183,428   (C) 142,428   (D) 242,428

3.   Which of these will result in the answer 23?

(A) 23,000 ÷ 10   (B) 23,000 ÷ 100

(C) 2,300 ÷ 100   (D) 230,000 ÷ 1,000

4.   Divide 4,825 by 23.

(A) 29 R 18   (B) 117 R 1   (C) 203 R 25   (D) 209 R 18

5.   Evaluate (45 − 21) ÷ 8 + 2.

(A) 5   (B) 7   (C) 8   (D) 12

Short Answer   (5 × 2 points = 10 points)

Multiply. Show your work.

6.   2,356 × 700

7.   8,093 × 56

Solve. Show your work.

8.   A rectangular wall measures 1,620 centimeters by 68 centimeters. Estimate the area of the wall.

9.   3,812 people are seated in a concert hall. There are 48 seats in each row. Estimate the number of rows of seats that are occupied.

10.   Tom had $8,153 in his bank account. He deposited another $847 into the account. He then used all his money to buy 100 identical cameras. He sold the cameras for $150 each. How much did Tom earn from selling each camera?

Extended Response (Question 11: 2 points, Question 12: 3 points)

Solve. Show your work.

11. 🖩 Mr. Jensen bought a set of furniture for $5,645. He paid $500 at first.
He then paid the remainder in equal payments, every month for 7 months.
How much did he pay each month?

12. 🖩 Jody paid $1.60 for each box of 35 beads.
She has 1,400 beads altogether.

   a. How much did Jody pay in all for the beads?

   b. Jody repacks the beads into small boxes with 16 beads in each box.
How many small boxes does she need?

Fractions and Mixed Numbers

Vocabulary

Fill in the blanks.
Use the words in the box.

1. $\frac{2}{3}$ and $\frac{1}{3}$ are _____.

2. 3 and 5 are _____.

3. $\frac{4}{5}$ and $\frac{8}{10}$ are _____.

4. $\frac{1}{4}$ and $\frac{1}{5}$ are _____.

> unlike fractions
>
> equivalent fractions
>
> prime numbers
>
> like fractions

Concepts and Skills

Write your answer in the space given.

5. Circle the like fractions in the set.

   $\frac{3}{10}$ $\frac{2}{7}$ $\frac{7}{10}$ $\frac{3}{4}$

6. Express each fraction in simplest form.

   a. $\frac{6}{10} = \dfrac{\Box}{\Box}$ **b.** $\frac{6}{18} = \dfrac{\Box}{\Box}$

7. Find the missing denominator in each fraction.

   a. $\frac{3}{8} = \dfrac{12}{\Box}$ **b.** $\frac{16}{20} = \dfrac{4}{\Box}$

8.   Circle the prime number.

6   18   23

9.   Circle the composite number.

5   9   47

10.   Circle the unlike fractions in the set.

$\frac{2}{7}$ $\frac{3}{8}$ $\frac{1}{3}$ $\frac{5}{8}$

11.   Express each improper fraction as a mixed number by using the division rule.

a. $\frac{17}{3}$ **b.** $\frac{23}{20}$

Add. Express the sum in simplest form.

12. $\frac{1}{3} + \frac{1}{12}$

13. $\frac{5}{8} + \frac{1}{4} + \frac{1}{2}$

Subtract. Express the difference in simplest form.

14. $\dfrac{7}{9} - \dfrac{1}{3}$

15. $3 - \dfrac{1}{2} - \dfrac{1}{6}$

Express each fraction as a decimal.

16. $\dfrac{6}{10} =$ _____

17. $\dfrac{74}{100} =$ _____

Problem Solving

Solve. Show your work.

18. Linus has a cake. He gives $\frac{3}{5}$ of the cake to Fred and $\frac{1}{10}$ of the cake to Ron. What fraction of the cake does Linus have?

19. Harris has $\frac{4}{5}$ kilogram of raisins. He buys another $\frac{3}{10}$ kilogram of raisins. How many kilograms of raisins does he have now?

Name: _____   Date: _____

Fractions and Mixed Numbers

Multiple Choice   (5 × 2 points = 10 points)

Fill in the circle next to the correct answer.

1. Which fraction has the same value as $\frac{3}{5} + \frac{1}{3}$?

(A) $\frac{2}{15}$ (B) $\frac{4}{15}$ (C) $\frac{1}{2}$ (D) $\frac{14}{15}$

2. What is the value of $\frac{7}{10} - \frac{3}{6}$?

(A) $\frac{1}{15}$ (B) $\frac{2}{15}$ (C) $\frac{1}{5}$ (D) 1

3. What is 25 ÷ 7 expressed as a mixed number?

(A) $3\frac{4}{7}$ (B) $\frac{25}{7}$ (C) $2\frac{5}{7}$ (D) $5\frac{2}{7}$

4. Which fraction has the same value as 0.65?

(A) $\frac{65}{10}$ (B) $\frac{65}{50}$ (C) $\frac{13}{20}$ (D) $\frac{26}{50}$

5. Mrs. Olive used $1\frac{2}{5}$ quarts of syrup and $5\frac{3}{10}$ quarts of water to make lemonade.

How many quarts of lemonade did she make?

(A) $6\frac{1}{2}$ (B) $6\frac{7}{10}$ (C) $7\frac{1}{2}$ (D) 8

Short Answer   (5 × 2 points = 10 points)

Add or subtract. Express each sum or difference in simplest form.

6.   **a.** $2\frac{3}{4} + 3\frac{2}{5}$ **b.** $3\frac{1}{2} - 1\frac{7}{8}$

Estimate each sum or difference by using benchmarks.

7.   **a.** $\frac{1}{4} + \frac{7}{12} + \frac{2}{3}$ **b.** $\frac{4}{5} - \frac{3}{7}$

Solve. Show your work.

8.   Gail baked some cookies. She sold $\frac{2}{7}$ of the cookies on Monday.

She sold $\frac{1}{3}$ more of the cookies on Tuesday than on Monday.

What fraction of the cookies did Gail sell on the two days?

Solve. Show your work.

9. Katie has a roll of ribbon that is 8 feet long. She cuts off 3 feet of ribbon and the remaining length is cut into 8 shorter pieces of equal length. What is the length of each shorter piece of ribbon?

10. An organic farm uses $\frac{3}{7}$ of the land to grow potatoes and $\frac{2}{5}$ of the land to grow spinach. The remaining land is used to grow tomato plants. What fraction of the land is used to grow tomato plants?

Extended Response (Question 11: 2 points, Question 12: 3 points)

Solve. Show your work.

11. Jenny uses $\frac{7}{9}$ gallon of water to water roses.

    She uses $\frac{1}{4}$ gallon less water to water herbs.

    How much water does Jenny use to water the roses and herbs?

12. Julian and Stacey needed 10 liters of water to fill a tank. Stacey filled the tank with $3\frac{11}{12}$ liters of water. Julian poured $1\frac{2}{5}$ liters less than Stacey into the tank. How much more water is still needed to fill the tank?

Multiplying and Dividing Fractions and Mixed Numbers

Vocabulary

Fill in the blanks.
Use the words in the box.

1. To _____ a fraction is to reduce it to simplest form.

2. In an _____, the numerator is greater than the denominator.

3. To express a fraction as a _____, change its denominator to 10 or 100 first.

decimal
simplify
improper fraction

Concepts and Skills

Write your answer in the space given.

4. Circle the equivalent fractions.

    $\frac{2}{9}$ $\frac{1}{3}$ $\frac{4}{18}$ $\frac{6}{27}$ $\frac{3}{10}$

Simplify.

5. $\frac{15}{18}$ 6. $\frac{14}{35}$

Complete. Show your work.

7.   Subtract $\frac{3}{10}$ from 3.

8.   Express each improper fraction as a mixed number.

   a. $\frac{15}{4}$ **b.** $\frac{21}{5}$

9.   Express $5\frac{2}{5}$ as an improper fraction.

10.   Express $\frac{3}{5}$ as a decimal.

11.   Find the product of $\frac{2}{3}$ and 36.

12.   Simplify $25 \times 4 \div (12 - 8)$.

Draw a model to show what is stated.

13. Gomez spent $\frac{5}{8}$ of his money on a gift for his brother and $\frac{1}{6}$ of his money on a card. He saved the rest of his money.

Solve.

14. Lisa paid $18 for 9 cupcakes.
How much do 6 cupcakes cost?

Problem Solving

Solve. Show your work.

15. Kim has 18 toys. $\frac{1}{3}$ of the toys are teddy bears. $\frac{1}{6}$ of the toys are balls and the rest are dolls. How many dolls does Kim have?

16. Sally has 6 boxes of colored pencils. Only 3 of the boxes contain 12 colored pencils each. The remaining boxes each contain 20 colored pencils. She packs the colored pencils into 8 packets. How many pencils are there in each packet?

TEST PREP 4

Multiplying and Dividing Fractions and Mixed Numbers

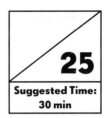

25

Suggested Time: 30 min

Multiple Choice (5 × 2 points = 10 points)

Fill in the circle next to the correct answer.

1. Multiply $\frac{4}{5}$ by $\frac{15}{16}$. Give your answer in simplest form.

   (A) $\frac{3}{4}$ (B) $\frac{60}{80}$ (C) $\frac{19}{21}$ (D) $\frac{20}{21}$

2. Which has the same value as $\frac{5}{8} \div 3$?

   (A) $\frac{5}{8} \times \frac{3}{1}$ (B) $\frac{8}{5} \times \frac{3}{1}$ (C) $\frac{5}{8} \times \frac{1}{3}$ (D) $\frac{8}{5} \times \frac{1}{3}$

3. Joe has $\frac{8}{9}$ kilogram of clay. He uses $\frac{3}{4}$ of it to make a vase.
   How much clay is left?

   (A) $\frac{5}{36}$ kg   (B) $\frac{23}{36}$ kg   (C) $\frac{2}{9}$ kg   (D) $\frac{7}{9}$ kg

4. Daisy has $5\frac{1}{2}$ pounds of chocolate. She uses $\frac{4}{5}$ of it to bake brownies. How much chocolate does she use to bake brownies?

   (A) $2\frac{1}{5}$ lb   (B) $2\frac{2}{5}$ lb   (C) $3\frac{3}{7}$ lb   (D) $4\frac{2}{5}$ lb

5. Claire picked some apples. She used $\frac{2}{5}$ of the apples to make jam. She gave $\frac{1}{3}$ of the remainder to her neighbor. What fraction of the apples did she give to her neighbor?

   (A) $\frac{2}{15}$ (B) $\frac{1}{5}$ (C) $\frac{2}{5}$ (D) $\frac{3}{5}$

Short Answer (5 × 2 points = 10 points)

Multiply or divide. Express your answer in simplest form.

6. **a.** $5\frac{5}{8} \times 18$ **b.** $\frac{3}{8} \div 12$

Solve. Show your work.

7. Jill had $\frac{4}{5}$ meter of cloth. She cut it into 8 equal pieces. What is the length of each piece?

8. Tom works $1\frac{3}{4}$ hours a day at a café. He is paid $8 an hour. How much money is he paid in 10 days?

Solve. Show your work.

9.   Tyron takes $\frac{3}{4}$ hour to paint a wall. His brother takes $\frac{1}{3}$ of the time he takes. How long will his brother take to paint 5 similar walls?

10.   Susan has $80. She spends $\frac{3}{5}$ of the money on Monday. She spends the remaining money equally over the next 5 days. How much money does she spend on each of the 5 days?

Extended Response   (Question 11: 2 points, Question 12: 3 points)

Solve. Show your work.

11. Lisa has some clips. $\frac{1}{4}$ of the clips are pink, $\frac{1}{3}$ of the remainder are blue, and the rest are yellow. What fraction of the clips are yellow?

12. Klein read 30 pages of a book on Monday and $\frac{1}{8}$ of the book on Tuesday. He completed the remaining $\frac{1}{4}$ of the book on Wednesday. How many pages are there in the book?

Benchmark Assessment 1
for Chapters 1 to 4

50

Suggested Time:
45 min

Multiple Choice   (10 × 2 points = 20 points)

Fill in the circle next to the correct answer.

1. Estimate the product of 1,398 and 8 by rounding to the nearest thousand.

Ⓐ 6,000   Ⓑ 8,000   Ⓒ 9,000   Ⓓ 12,000

2. Find the sum of the value of 8 in 387,562 and the value of 7 in 7,328,562.

Ⓐ 1,500   Ⓑ 7,800   Ⓒ 7,800,000   Ⓓ 7,080,000

3. Find the value of 56 + 9 − (18 ÷ 6) × 2.

Ⓐ 53   Ⓑ 59   Ⓒ 62   Ⓓ 124

4. A supermarket has 64 cartons of 40 peaches. The peaches are packed into bags of 8 each. How many bags of peaches are there?

Ⓐ 105   Ⓑ 140   Ⓒ 320   Ⓓ 336

5. A van cost $72,655. Mr. Smith paid a deposit of $66,655 and he will pay the rest in 12 equal payments. How much does he have to pay for each payment?

Ⓐ $500   Ⓑ $2,000   Ⓒ $5,000   Ⓓ $6,000

6. Adam's father is 3 times as old as Adam. Two years ago, Adam was 15 years old. How old will his father be in 5 years?

(A) 44 years   (B) 50 years   (C) 51 years   (D) 56 years

7. What is the value of $\frac{9}{5} \times \frac{1}{3}$?

(A) $\frac{3}{5}$ (B) $1\frac{7}{15}$ (C) $2\frac{2}{15}$ (D) $5\frac{2}{5}$

8. Claire has $\frac{3}{2}$ liters of water. She pours the water equally into 6 glasses. How much water is in each glass?

(A) $\frac{1}{4}$ L   (B) $1\frac{1}{12}$ L   (C) $7\frac{1}{2}$ L   (D) 9 L

9. Write the product of $\frac{7}{20}$ and 3 as a decimal.

(A) 0.86   (B) 0.95   (C) 1.05   (D) 2.1

10. Alice has $560 in the bank. She uses $\frac{1}{4}$ of it to buy a bag and $\frac{2}{3}$ of the remaining money to buy a present for her mother. How much money does Alice have left?

(A) $70   (B) $140   (C) $208   (D) $420

Short Answer (10 × 2 points = 20 points)

Write your answer in the space given.

11.   Find the value of the digit 7 in 6,734,254.   _____

12.   Use these digits to make the least 6-digit even number.

        6, 1, 4, 7, 2, 8

        _____

13.   Billy wants to buy 657 mugs. The mugs are sold for a price of 3 for $4.
        How much must Billy pay for all the mugs?

14.   There are 15 groups of people at a function. Each group has 32 people in it.
        The people are then regrouped into 16 equal groups. How many people are
        there in each group now?

15. Find the value of $3\frac{2}{5} + 9\frac{4}{15}$.

16. Express the value of $\frac{6}{25} \times \frac{3}{4}$ as a decimal.

17. Belinda has a bag of beads. She uses $\frac{1}{3}$ of the beads to make a bracelet and $\frac{3}{5}$ of the beads to make a necklace. She uses 36 more beads to make the necklace. How many beads does Belinda use to make the bracelet?

18. Jenny baked some biscuits. The first batch of biscuits she baked contained $1\frac{2}{3}$ pounds of biscuits and the second batch contained $2\frac{1}{2}$ pounds of biscuits. How many pounds of biscuits did she bake in all?

19. The length of a rectangle is $\frac{2}{5}$ meter. Its width is $\frac{1}{4}$ of its length. What is the perimeter of the rectangle?

20. A travel company has 132 tourists who are going on a boat ride. Each boat holds 8 passengers. How many boats does the travel company need to book?

Extended Response

(Question 21 and 22: 2 × 3 points = 6 points, Question 23: 4 points)

Solve. Show your work.

21. Patrick has $1\frac{1}{2}$ liters of blue paint and $3\frac{3}{5}$ liters of red paint. He mixes $\frac{2}{3}$ of the blue paint and $\frac{5}{6}$ of the red paint to get purple paint. How much purple paint does Patrick have?

22. Mrs. Sanchez has a bag of assorted nuts that contain almonds, pecans, and walnuts. $\frac{1}{3}$ of the nuts are almonds and $\frac{3}{4}$ of the remainder are pecans. There are 300 nuts in the bag. How many walnuts are in the bag?

Solve. Show your work.

23. Mr. and Mrs. Jefferson have a total of $5,170 in a bank. At the end of the month, Mr. Jefferson deposits $450 into his account, and Mrs. Jefferson deposits $626 into her account. They now have an equal amount of money in their accounts. How much money did each of them have at first?

Bonus Questions

Solve. Show your work.

1. Leslie has 10 small gift cards. Some are square in shape and some are triangular. The cards have 34 sides altogether. How many square cards does Leslie have?

Solve. Show your work.

2. A grocer had some eggs. When he packed them into **groups of 4**, there were **3 eggs left over**. When he packed them into **groups of 5**, there were **2 eggs left over**. When he packed them into **groups of 9**, there were **no eggs left over**. Find the least number of eggs the grocer had.

Vocabulary

Fill in the blanks.
Use the words in the box.

1. _____ are operations that have opposite effects.

2. What do these symbols mean?

   = _____

   > _____

   < _____

| greater than |
| equal |
| less than |
| inverse operations |
| order of operations |

3. This is the _____ to simplify an expression:

   Step 1 Work inside the parenthesis.

   Step 2 Multiply and divide from left to right.

   Step 3 Add and subtract from left to right.

Concepts and Skills

Write =, >, or < in the ◯.

4. 35 ◯ 93

5. 41 + 32 ◯ 90 − 17

6. $\frac{1}{2}$ ◯ $\frac{3}{4}$

7. 16 × 4 ◯ 183 ÷ 3

Complete.

8. 5 × ☐ = 9 + 9 + 9 + 9 + 9

9. 2 × 32 = ☐ + ☐

Find the missing number.

10. 6 × ☐ = 72

11. ☐ − 23 = 53

12. ☐ ÷ 7 = 20

13. 40 + ☐ = 64

14. **Simplify the expression.**

2 + (7 − 4) × 3

Problem Solving

Solve. Show your work.

15. Adam has 95 mangoes. He packs 15 mangoes into a box and the remaining into plastic bags of 10 mangoes each. How many plastic bags does he need?

 **Algebra**

25

Suggested Time:
30 min

Multiple Choice   (5 × 2 points = 10 points)

Fill in the circle next to the correct answer.

1. What does 8y mean?

Ⓐ $8 + y$ Ⓑ $8 \times y$ Ⓒ $8 \div y$ Ⓓ $8 - y$

2. Florence makes y cards in 3 minutes. How many cards does she make in 1 minute?

Ⓐ $\frac{3}{y}$ Ⓑ $\frac{1}{y}$ Ⓒ $\frac{y}{3}$ Ⓓ y

3. Divide the sum of 18 and z by 7.

Which is the expression for the above division statement?

Ⓐ $\frac{18 + z}{7}$ Ⓑ $\frac{18 + 7}{z}$

Ⓒ $z \div 7 + 18$ Ⓓ $18 + z \div 7$

4. What is the value of the expression $\frac{3p}{8} + 4$ when p is 32?

Ⓐ 8   Ⓑ 12   Ⓒ 12.5   Ⓓ 16

5. For what value of x will $6x - 3 > 2x + 15$ be true?

Ⓐ $x = 1$ Ⓑ $x = 2$ Ⓒ $x = 4$ Ⓓ $x = 5$

Short Answer   (5 × 2 points = 10 points)

Write your answer in the space given.

6.   Write the expression for 100 less than the sum of 3 and x.

_____

7.   Harris has \$60. He spends y dollars. How much money does he have left? Give your answer in terms of y.

Simplify each expression.

8.   **a.** $15y + 2 - y + 3y + 6$ **b.** $(z - 24) \div 8 + 2$

Complete with =, >, or < for $x = 9$.

9.   **a.** $4x + 3 \bigcirc \dfrac{100x}{20}$ **b.** $(100 - 2x) \div 2 \bigcirc 4 \times (x + 1)$

Solve each equation.

10.   **a.** $18m - 52 = 5m$ **b.** $4p + 8 = 12p - 16$

Extended Response   (Question 11: 2 points, Question 12: 3 points)

Solve. Show your work.

11. Cheryl has some oranges. She puts the oranges into p boxes of 3 oranges each and has 2 oranges left.

   a. Find the total number of oranges Cheryl has in terms of p.

   b. If $p = 6$, how many oranges does Cheryl have?

12. Ernie read $3y + 4$ books. Gladice read $4y - 5$ books.

   a. If $y = 3$, who read more books?

   b. For what value of y will both of them read the same number of books?

PRE-TEST 6 — Area of a Triangle

Vocabulary

Fill in the blanks.
Use the words in the box.

1. _____ is the amount of surface covered.

2. Area is measured in _____.

3. _____ have three straight sides.

4. The area of a rectangle can be found using a _____.

> triangles
> formula
> square units
> area

Concepts and Skills

Write your answer in the space given.

5. Circle the shapes that are triangles.

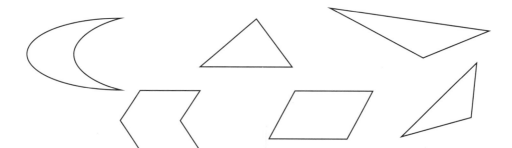

6. Classify the angles in the triangle as an acute angle, right angle, or an obtuse angle.

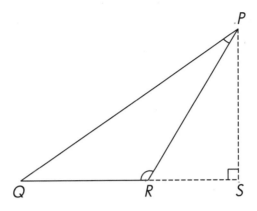

a. ∠PRQ   _____

b. ∠PSR   _____

c. ∠QPR   _____

Check (✔) the box that shows perpendicular line segments.

7. **a.**

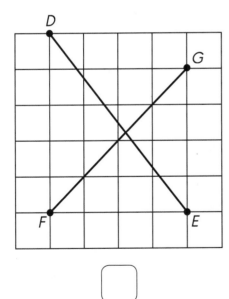

b.

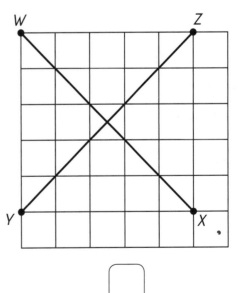

Shade the area of each figure.

8.

Find the area of each figure.

9.

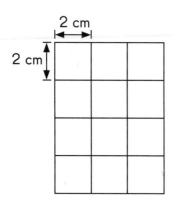

2 cm

2 cm

Area = _____

10.

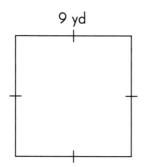

1 in.

1 in.

Area = _____

11.

25 ft

7 ft

Area = _____

12.

9 yd

Area = _____

13.

17 m

40 m

Area = _____

Problem Solving

Solve. Show your work.

14. A garden has the same area as a rectangular wall that measures 3 meters by 2 meters. What is the area of the garden?

15. A square plot of land has a side length of 50 meters.
It is surrounded by a footpath that is 3 meters wide.
What is the area of the footpath?

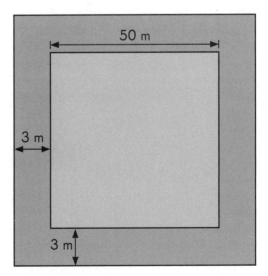

Area of a Triangle

TEST PREP 6

25

Suggested Time:
30 min

Multiple Choice (5 × 2 points = 10 points)

Fill in the circle next to the correct answer.

1. Which is the base of the triangle *ABC* when the height is $\overline{BZ}$?

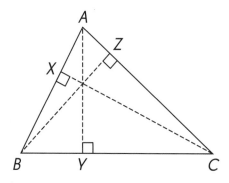

(A) $\overline{AB}$ (B) $\overline{AC}$ (C) $\overline{CX}$ (D) $\overline{BC}$

2. In the shaded triangle, which is the base if the height is $\overline{DC}$?

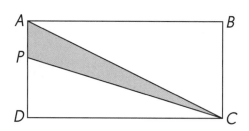

(A) $\overline{PC}$ (B) $\overline{BC}$ (C) $\overline{AC}$ (D) $\overline{AP}$

3.   What is the area of the triangle?

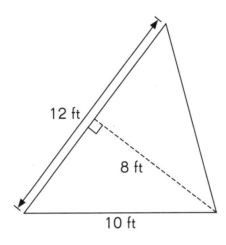

(A) 48 ft²   (B) 60 ft²   (C) 80 ft²   (D) 96 ft²

4.   Which triangle has an area of 36 cm²?

Ⓐ
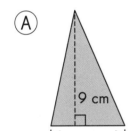

Ⓑ
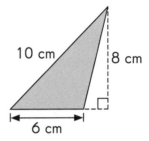

Ⓒ
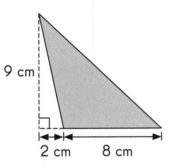

Ⓓ
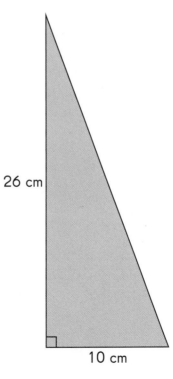

5.   Find the area of the shaded part of the figure.

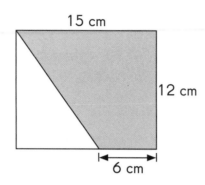

15 cm

12 cm

6 cm

A 144 cm² B 126 cm² C 54 cm² D 36 cm²

Short Answer   (5 × 2 points = 10 points)

Write your answer in the space given.

6.   Draw the height of the triangle.

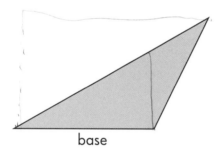

base

7.   Name the base and height of the triangle.

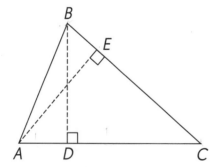

In triangle *BCD*,

Base: _____

Height: _____

8. Find the area of the shaded triangle *CDE*.
ABCD is a square that has a side length of 24 meters.

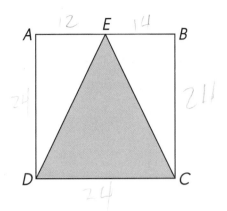

9. Find the area of the shaded triangle.

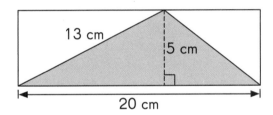

10. Find the area of the shaded part.

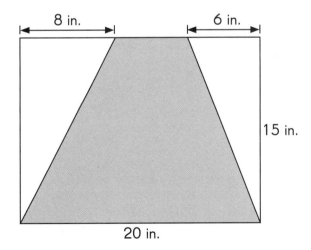

Extended Response   (Question 11: 2 points, Question 12: 3 points)

Solve. Show your work.

11. The figure is made up of 3 identical rectangles measuring 8 centimeters by 3 centimeters. Find the area of the shaded part of the figure.

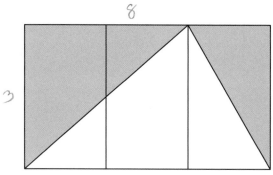

12. The perimeter of the rectangle is 60 meters. Find the area of the shaded part of the figure.

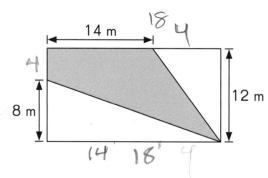

PRE-TEST 7 Ratio

Vocabulary

Fill in the blanks.
Use the words in the box.

1. In a fraction, the _____ represents the number

   of parts and the _____ represents the whole.

bar model
numerator
denominator

2. A _____ can be used to help solve word problems.

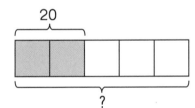

From the model,
2 units → 20
1 unit → 20 ÷ 2 = 10
5 units → 10 × 5 = 50

Concepts and Skills

Complete each number bond.

3. 16 − 9

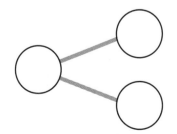

4. 25 − 18

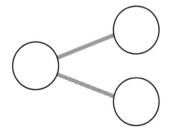

State how many parts of the whole are represented by each fraction.

5. $\frac{2}{7}$

_____

6. $\frac{8}{9}$

_____

Write each fraction in simplest form.

7. $\frac{9}{12}$

8. $\frac{24}{60}$

Find the value of each set using the model.

9. A = _____

B = _____

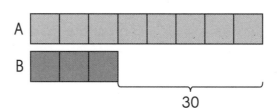

Problem Solving

Solve. Show your work.

10. Tom has three times as many stamps as Lisa. Lisa has 22 stamps. How many more stamps does Tom have than Lisa?

 **Ratio**

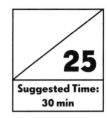

25

Suggested Time:
30 min

Multiple Choice   (5 × 2 points = 10 points)

Fill in the circle next to the correct answer.

1. There are 8 apples in a box. Of the apples, 3 are red and the rest are green. What is the ratio of the number of red apples to the number of green apples?

(A) 3 : 5   (B) 5 : 3   (C) 8 : 3   (D) 8 : 5

2. Look at the table.

Class	Number of Students
A	40
B	36
C	32
D	44

What is the ratio of the number of students in class B to the number of students in class A? Give your answer in simplest form.

(A) 8 : 10   (B) 8 : 11   (C) 9 : 10   (D) 10 : 9

3. Find the unknown value in 4 : 5 = 16 : ☐

(A) 25   (B) 20   (C) 17   (D) 9

4. The total length of 3 blocks is 50 meters. The length of block A is 15 centimeters and the length of block C is 20 centimeters. What is the ratio of the total length of the 3 blocks to the length of block B?

Ⓐ 1 : 1   Ⓑ 3 : 4   Ⓒ 3 : 10   Ⓓ 10 : 3

5. Nyan gives $24 to Mary and Linda in the ratio 1 : 3. How much money does Linda get?

Ⓐ $6   Ⓑ $12   Ⓒ $18   Ⓓ $24

Short Answer   (5 × 2 points = 10 points)

Write your answer in the space given.

6. Layla uses white beads and black beads to make three bracelets. How many times the number of black beads is the number of white beads?

7. Find the missing numbers in this set of equivalent ratios.

5 : ⬜ : 9 = ⬜ : 12 : 27

8.   The amount of time Ron spends on his computer is twice the amount of time he spends reading. What is the ratio of the time Ron spends reading to the time he spends on the computer to the total time he spends on both activities?

9.   The ratio of the number of apples to the number of oranges to the number of pears is 3 : 5 : 2. There are 15 oranges. How many fruits are there in all?

10.   The ratio of the ages of 3 children is 1 : 3 : 5. The oldest child is 12 years older than the youngest child. How old is the middle child?

Extended Response (Question 11: 2 points, Question 12: 3 points)

Solve. Show your work.

11.   Ken's mass is $\frac{5}{8}$ of John's mass. John's mass is 64 kilograms.

   a.   Find the ratio of Ken's mass to John's mass.

   b.   How much heavier is John than Ken?

12.   A door is painted pink and blue. The area painted pink is 4 times that of the area painted blue.

   a.   What is the ratio of the area that is painted blue to the area that is painted pink?

   b.   The door has an area of 5 square meters. Find the area of the part of the door that is painted pink.

Mid-Year Test

Multiple Choice (10 × 2 points = 20 points)

```
50
```
Suggested Time:
45 min

Fill in the circle next to the correct answer.

1. Estimate 9,810 + 3,879 by rounding to the nearest thousand.

   (A) 12,000   (B) 13,700   (C) 14,000   (D) 15,000

2. What is the value of the digit 2 in 6,284,045?

   (A) 2,000   (B) 20,000   (C) 200,000   (D) 2,000,000

3. What is the value of $6 - 3\frac{4}{7}$?

   (A) $2\frac{3}{7}$ (B) $3\frac{4}{7}$ (C) $6\frac{3}{7}$ (D) $6\frac{4}{7}$

4. Pauline pours $\frac{9}{10}$ liter of juice equally into 6 bottles. How much juice is in each bottle?

   (A) $\frac{3}{20}$ L   (B) $\frac{5}{12}$ L   (C) $2\frac{1}{2}$ L   (D) $5\frac{2}{5}$ L

5. Ellen uses $\frac{2}{7}$ of her money to pay for a book. She uses $\frac{2}{5}$ of the remaining money to pay for a bag. Ellen has $15 left. How much money did she have at first?

   (A) $25   (B) $35   (C) $49   (D) $50

6.   Find the value that belongs in each box.

$$2 : 3 : \boxed{\text{A}} = 10 : \boxed{\text{B}} : 35$$

(A) A = 5, B = 6   (B) A = 7, B = 9

(C) A = 5, B = 25   (D) A = 7, B = 15

7.   1 meter of cloth is cut into 3 pieces. One piece is 40 centimeters long and another piece is 35 centimeters long. What is the ratio of the length of the shortest piece to the length of the longest piece?

(A) 4 : 5   (B) 5 : 7   (C) 5 : 8   (D) 7 : 8

8.   Which expression shows 2 more than the product of 4x and 3?

(A) $4x - 3 + 2$ (B) $12x + 2$ (C) $\frac{4x}{3} + 2$ (D) $\frac{4x + 2}{3}$

9.   There are 10 boys and some girls in a class. There are 8 more girls than boys. How many times the number of girls is the number of students in the class?

(A) $\frac{5}{4}$ (B) $\frac{5}{9}$ (C) $\frac{9}{14}$ (D) $\frac{14}{9}$

10.   Find the area of the triangle.

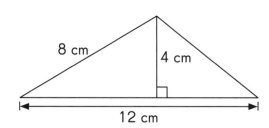

8 cm   4 cm   12 cm

(A) 16 cm²   (B) 24 cm²   (C) 32 cm²   (D) 48 cm²

Short Answer   (10 × 2 points = 20 points)

Write your answer in the space given.

11. Find the missing number in the pattern.

3,952,560 4,032,560 4,112,560 _____

12. Estimate the product of 6,315 and 72 by rounding each factor to the nearest ten or thousand.

13. Simplify 32 + (25 ÷ 5) − 21 ÷ 7.

14. Find the value of $\frac{4}{5}$ ÷ 20. Express your answer as a decimal.

15. A CD player costs $12. It is $\frac{1}{3}$ of the cost of a radio. How much does the radio cost?

16. Matthew takes $2\frac{3}{4}$ hours to complete a project. Peter takes $\frac{1}{5}$ hour less than Matthew to complete his project. What is the total time it takes to complete both projects?

17. Find the area of the shaded part of the figure.

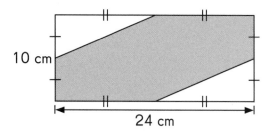

10 cm

24 cm

18. James and Jerry sold *x* pens at a carnival. They sold 5 times as many rulers as pens. They sold 3 less pencils than pens. Write an expression, in terms of *x*, for the total number of items they sold at the carnival.

19. Jim is twice as old as Tammy. Sandy is $\frac{1}{4}$ the age of Tammy. What is the ratio of Jim's age to Tammy's age to Sandy's age?

20. Find the area of the shaded part of the figure.

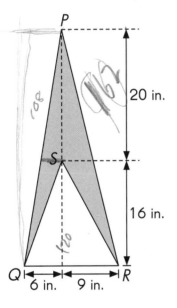

Extended Response

(Question 21 and 22: 2 × 3 points = 6 points, Question 23: 4 points)

Solve. Show your work.

21. The ratio of the number of quarters to dimes in a savings box is 10 : 3. The total amount of money in the box is $22.40. How many quarters and dimes are there?

22. 1 box of crayons and 3 erasers cost $10.
3 boxes of crayons and 3 erasers cost $18.
Find the total cost of 1 box of crayons and 1 eraser.

23. A bookshop has some fiction and non-fiction books. $\frac{2}{5}$ of the books are fiction books. Of these, $\frac{1}{5}$ are mystery stories. $\frac{1}{3}$ of the non-fiction books are mystery stories too. What fraction of all the books in the shop are mystery books?

Bonus Questions

Solve. Show your work.

1. The figure is made up of 2 identical isosceles triangles. The shaded part is a square with sides measuring 5 centimeters. Find the area of the unshaded part of the figure.

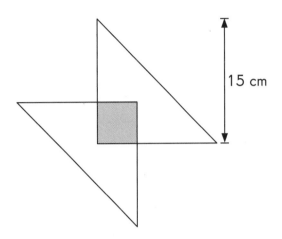

15 cm

2. 10 trees were planted in a row equal distances apart. The distance between the first tree and the fourth tree is $\frac{3}{5}$ meter. Calculate the distance between the first tree and the tenth tree.

Decimals

Vocabulary

Fill in the blanks.
Use the words in the box.

1. $\frac{6}{10}$ is 6 _____.

2. $\frac{3}{100}$ is 3 _____.

3. When rounding a decimal to the _____, check the value of the tenths digit.

4. When rounding a decimal to the _____, round to the lesser tenth if the hundredths digit is 0, 1, 2, 3, or 4.

5. Like comparing whole numbers, compare _____ by checking the value of their digits from left to right.

tenths
decimals
hundredths
nearest whole number
nearest tenth

Concepts and Skills

Write the decimal that each marked point represents.

6. a.

    b.

_____   _____

Write the decimal that each place-value chart represents.

7.   a.

Ones	Tenths
○	○ ○ ○ ○ ○ ○

_____

   b.

Ones	Tenths	Hundredths
○ ○ ○	○ ○	○ ○ ○ ○ ○ ○ ○ ○

_____

Which decimal is greater?

8.   3.82 or 4.13   _____

9.   9.15 or 9.2   _____

Express each fraction or mixed number as a decimal.

10. $\frac{3}{20}$ _____

11. $3\frac{17}{50}$ _____

Round each decimal to the nearest whole number and then to the nearest tenth.

12.   2.70   _____ ; _____

13.   5.19   _____ ; _____

14.   9.63   _____ ; _____

15.   1.04   _____ ; _____

16.   7.85   _____ ; _____

17.   2.96   _____ ; _____

Problem Solving

Solve. Show your work.

18. Jessie bought a piece of ribbon that was $1\frac{2}{5}$ meters long. She cut $\frac{17}{20}$ meter from it. What is the length of the remaining piece of ribbon? Give your answer as a decimal to the nearest tenth.

Decimals

25

Suggested Time:
30 min

Multiple Choice (5 × 2 points = 10 points)

Fill in the circle next to the correct answer.

1. Which decimal do the shaded parts represent?

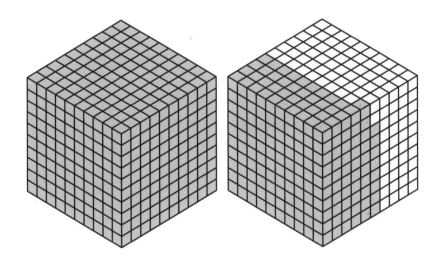

Ⓐ 0.418

Ⓑ 1.418

Ⓒ 1.148

Ⓓ 4.18

2. What is the place value of the digit 3 in 8.139?

Ⓐ tens   Ⓑ tenths   Ⓒ hundredths   Ⓓ thousandths

3. Which of these decimals is the greatest?

Ⓐ 21.07   Ⓑ 2.107   Ⓒ 1.973   Ⓓ 27.6

4. Round 5.693 to the nearest hundredth.

Ⓐ 5.69   Ⓑ 5.68   Ⓒ 5.7   Ⓓ 5.70

5. Write 6.04 as a mixed number in simplest form.

Ⓐ $6\frac{2}{5}$ Ⓑ $6\frac{1}{25}$ Ⓒ $6\frac{4}{100}$ Ⓓ $6\frac{64}{100}$

Name: _____   Date: _____

Show the location of each decimal by drawing an X on the number line.

6.   **a.**   0.014   **b.**   0.038

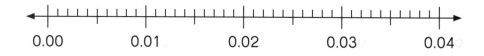

| 0.00 | 0.01 | 0.02 | 0.03 | 0.04 |

Write each mixed number as a decimal.

7.   **a.** $5\frac{18}{1000} =$ _____   **b.** $2\frac{349}{1000} =$ _____

Order the decimals from least to greatest.

8.   6.63   3.6   10.1   3.178

_____

Complete.

9. $8.275 = 8 + 0.2 +$ _____ $+$ _____

Solve.

10.   A decimal has three decimal places. The decimal, rounded to the nearest tenth, is 1.6. What is the greatest possible decimal that can be rounded to 1.6?

Extended Response

(Question 11: 2 points, Question 12: 3 points)

Solve. Show your work.

11. To make fruit punch, Mrs. Casey adds 1,200 milliliters of water to 850 milliliters of syrup. How many liters of fruit punch does she make? Give your answer in liters.

12. The height of a vase is 6.2 feet when rounded to the nearest tenth of a foot. What is the shortest possible height of the vase? Give your answer to 3 decimal places.

Multiplying and Dividing Decimals

Vocabulary

Fill in the blanks.
Use the words in the box.

1. When a whole number is _____,
    each digit of the number moves 1 place to
    the left in the place-value chart.

    > estimation
    >
    > multiplied by 10
    >
    > divided by 1,000

2. When a whole number is _____,
    each digit of the number moves 3 places to
    the right in the place-value chart.

3. Use _____ to check if the answer from a calculation
    is reasonable.

Concepts and Skills

Multiply.

4. 37×10

5. 136×100

6. $85 \times 1,000$

7. 92×30

8. 381×500

9. $76 \times 8,000$

Divide.

10.   6,400 ÷ 10

11.   3,900 ÷ 100

12.   8,000 ÷ 1,000

13.   540 ÷ 90

14.   6,300 ÷ 700

15.   72,000 ÷ 8,000

Estimate.

16.   Estimate the product of 623 and 59.

17.   Estimate the quotient of 9,842 and 36.

Name: _____ Date: _____

Problem Solving

Solve. Show your work.

18. A box of buttons costs $7.65. A piece of fabric costs $16.25 more than the box of buttons. Suzanne bought the box of buttons and the piece of fabric. She gave the cashier $50.

    a. What is the total amount Suzanne paid for the items?

    b. How much change did she get?

19. There are 208 rows of roses. Mr. Thomas plants 50 roses in each row.

    a. How many roses are there in all?

    b. Mr. Thomas harvests the roses and packs them into boxes. He packs 20 roses into each box. How many boxes does he need?

TEST PREP 9 Multiplying and Dividing Decimals

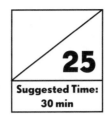

25

Suggested Time: 30 min

Multiple Choice   (5 × 2 points = 10 points)

Fill in the circle next to the correct answer.

1. Multiply 2.68 by 8.

(A) 2.144   (B) 21.44   (C) 214.4   (D) 2,144

2. What number belongs in the box?

7.31 × ☐ = 2,193

(A) 3   (B) 30   (C) 300   (D) 3,000

3. Divide 72.38 by 70.

(A) 1.034   (B) 1.304   (C) 10.34   (D) 103.4

4. A stack of 4 identical books is 6.28 inches high. What is the height of 30 of these books?

(A) 1.57 inches   (B) 4.7 inches

(C) 15.7 inches   (D) 47.1 inches

5. Alice ran 5 laps around a track. She ran a total distance of 3.65 kilometers. Jim ran 20 laps around the same track. What is the total distance Jim ran?

(A) 0.73 km   (B) 1.46 km   (C) 14.6 km   (D) 146 km

Short Answer (5 × 2 points = 10 points)

Find the missing number for each box.

6. a. $32.91 \times \boxed{} = 32{,}910$

  b. $11{,}845 \div 500 = 2{,}369 \div \boxed{}$

Multiply.

7.
$$
\begin{array}{r}
6\ .\ 8\quad 4 \\
\times \qquad\quad 7 \\
\hline
\boxed{\ }\ \boxed{\ }\ \boxed{\ }\ \boxed{\ }
\end{array}
$$

Estimate each sum or difference by rounding to the nearest whole number.

8. a. $23.63 + 15.3$

  b. $17.85 - 9.49$

Name: _____ **Date:** _____

Solve.

9. A piece of rope is 5 meters long. It is cut into 8 equal pieces. How long is each piece? Round your answer to the nearest hundredth.

10. A bag of flour weighs 15 pounds. A shopkeeper has one bag of flour. She sells 1.065 pounds of flour every day. How much flour is left after 8 days?

Extended Response   (Question 11: 2 points, Question 12: 3 points)

Solve. Show your work.

11.   Jai bought 2 pounds of grapes for $2.49 per pound and 3 muffins for $0.75 per muffin. How much did he pay for the grapes and muffins?

12.   Mr. Romero buys 3 chairs at a cost of $27.90 for each chair. Estimate the least number of $20 bills he needs to buy the chairs.

Percent

Vocabulary

Fill in the blanks.
Use the words in the box.

1. $\frac{27}{100}$ means 27 _____ 100.

2. $\frac{5}{100}$ expressed as a _____ is 0.05.

3. 0.48 expressed as a _____ is $\frac{48}{100}$.

4. The _____ fraction of $\frac{7}{20}$ that has a

    _____ of 100 is $\frac{35}{100}$.

equivalent
decimal
out of
denominator
fraction

Concepts and Skills

Express each fraction as a decimal.

5.

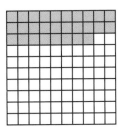

$\frac{28}{100} = $ _____

6.

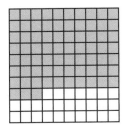

$\frac{73}{100} = $ _____

Express as a fraction with a denominator of 100.

7. 19 out of 100 = $\dfrac{\boxed{}}{\boxed{}}$

8. 91 out of 100 = $\dfrac{\boxed{}}{\boxed{}}$

Complete.

9. $\dfrac{3}{40}$ is _____ out of _____.

10. $\dfrac{79}{100}$ is _____ out of _____.

11. 0.58 is _____ out of _____.

12. 0.32 is _____ out of _____.

Find the missing numerators and denominators.

13. $\dfrac{9}{12} = \dfrac{3}{\boxed{}} = \dfrac{\boxed{}}{100}$

14. $\dfrac{4}{\boxed{}} = \dfrac{16}{\boxed{}} = \dfrac{28}{49}$

15. $\dfrac{2}{5} = \dfrac{4}{\boxed{}} = \dfrac{18}{\boxed{}}$

16. $\dfrac{9}{25} = \dfrac{18}{\boxed{}} = \dfrac{\boxed{}}{100}$

Express each fraction in simplest form.

17. $\dfrac{28}{50} =$ _____

18. $\dfrac{15}{20} =$ _____

19. $\dfrac{35}{70} =$ _____

20. $\dfrac{80}{100} =$ _____

Find the missing fractions or decimals.

21.

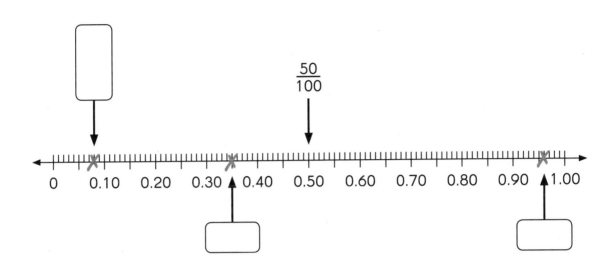

$\dfrac{50}{100}$

Problem Solving

Solve. Show your work.

22. Mrs. Gonzales uses 1.4 kilograms of flour and 300 grams of sugar to bake biscuits. What is the mass of the mixture of flour and sugar? Give your answer in kilograms.

Name: _____ **Date:** _____

Solve. Show your work.

23. Olive makes 2.4 liters of lemonade in a jug. She pours 1.75 liters of the lemonade into a bottle and spills 0.2 liter of it. How many liters of lemonade is left in the jug? Give your answer as a fraction.

Percent

25

Suggested Time:
30 min

Multiple Choice   (5 × 2 points = 10 points)

Fill in the circle next to the correct answer.

1.   0.25 is the same as _____.

(A) $\frac{1}{4}$%   (B) $\frac{22}{100}$%   (C) $2\frac{5}{10}$%   (D) 25%

2.   Express $\frac{18}{400}$ as a percent.

(A) 4.5%   (B) 7.2%   (C) 45%   (D) 72%

3.   Find 62% of 800.

(A) 862   (B) 738   (C) 496   (D) 180

4.   Of the 120 rooms in a hotel, 55% are single-bed rooms, 30% are double-bed rooms, and the rest are deluxe rooms. How many deluxe rooms are there?

(A) 15   (B) 18   (C) 36   (D) 66

5.   There are 600 spectators at a basketball game. 80% of the spectators are adults. Of the children, 10% are girls. How many girls are there?

(A) 480   (B) 120   (C) 36   (D) 12

Short Answer   (5 × 2 points = 10 points)

Write your answer in the space provided.

6. Express 45% as a fraction in simplest form.

Solve.

7. At a park, 80 out of the 200 people there are men. The rest are women. What percent of the people are women?

8. There are 680 students in a school. Of the students, 55% are girls and the rest are boys. How many more girls than boys are there in the school?

Solve.

9. In Lucy's bead collection, 75% of the beads are red, 12% are blue, and the rest are green. She has 104 green beads. How many blue beads does Lucy have?

10. Mr. Daniels earns $3,500 a month. He spends 72% of it and saves 25% of the remainder. The rest of the money is used to pay rent. How much is Mr. Daniels' rent?

Extended Response   (Question 11: 2 points, Question 12: 3 points)

Solve. Use models to help you.

11.   Emily wants to buy a car. She pays a deposit equal to 20% of the cost of the car. She will pay the balance in 8 equal payments of $5,460 each month. How much does the car cost?

12.   The regular price of an airline ticket was $1,200. At a travel company's 12th anniversary sale, Mr. Sims bought a ticket at a discount of 12%.

a.   What was the dollar amount of the discount?

b.   There was a 7% sales tax on the price of the ticket. How much did Mr. Sims pay for the ticket after the discount?

Benchmark Assessment 2
for Chapters 8 to 10

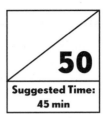

50

Suggested Time:
45 min

Multiple Choice   (10 × 2 points = 20 points)

Fill in the circle next to the correct answer.

1.   Round 8.693 to the nearest tenth.

Ⓐ 8.6   Ⓑ 8.7   Ⓒ 8.69   Ⓓ 9.0

2.   Which of these is greater than 10.5 but less than 20.1?

Ⓐ 0.105   Ⓑ 10.48   Ⓒ 12.865   Ⓓ 20.16

3.   Express 3.16 as a mixed number in simplest form.

Ⓐ $3\frac{1}{6}$ Ⓑ $3\frac{4}{25}$ Ⓒ $3\frac{2}{125}$ Ⓓ $\frac{316}{1000}$

4.   Find the value of 916 ÷ 800.

Ⓐ 114.5   Ⓑ 11.45   Ⓒ 1.145   Ⓓ 0.114

5.   Find the number that belongs in the box.

$\boxed{} \times 300 = 750$

Ⓐ 2.5   Ⓑ 4.5   Ⓒ 225   Ⓓ 250

6.   Mrs. Smith uses 18.6 pounds of flour to make 60 buns. How much flour does she use to make 12 buns?

 (A) 3.72 lb (B) 4.65 lb (C) 5.4 lb (D) 13.95 lb

7.   Express $\frac{1}{2}\%$ as a decimal.

 (A) 0.12 (B) 0.5 (C) 0.05 (D) 0.005

8.   Express $\frac{228}{400}$ as a percent.

 (A) 0.57% (B) 2.28% (C) 57% (D) 91.2%

9.   Of the 200 marbles Jenny has collected, 15% are white, 68% are multicolored, and the rest are black. How many black marbles does Jenny have?

 (A) 136 (B) 64 (C) 30 (D) 34

10.   The regular price of a dining table was $1,050. At a sale, Mrs. Carter bought the dining table at a discount of 30%. How much did she pay for the dining table?

 (A) $1,000 (B) $735 (C) $525 (D) $315

Short Answer (10 × 2 points = 20 points)

Write your answer in the space provided.

11. Write 3 tens and 25 thousandths as a decimal.

12. Express $\frac{9675}{1000}$ as a decimal. Round the decimal to the nearest whole number.

13. Express 7.065 as a mixed number in simplest form.

14. $900 \times 3.168 =$ _____

15. $6.24 \div 10 =$ _____ $\div\ 1,000$

Solve.

16.   Doris bought 8.75 pounds of chicken drumsticks. There are 36 drumsticks in all. Estimate the weight of each chicken drumstick.

17.   Of the 30 days in April, 6 days are school holidays. What percent of the days in April are not school holidays?

18.   Find the difference between 15% of $360 and 18% of $720.

Solve.

19. Leon used 2.1 liters of green paint to paint 42% of his room. He painted the remaining part of his room using brown paint. How many liters of brown paint did he use?

20. Andy, Jenny, and Suresh share a sum of money. Andy gets 20% and Jenny gets 10% more than Suresh. Suresh spends $\frac{3}{5}$ of his share. What percent of the total amount of money does Suresh have left?

Extended Response

(Question 21 and 22: 2 × 3 points = 6 points,
Question 23: 4 points)

Solve. Show your work.

21. A container and a jug had a total of 2.15 quarts of oil in them. When 0.18 quart of oil was poured from the container into the jug, the container had 4 times as much oil as the jug. How many quarts of oil were in the container at first?

22. A rope was 9.45 meters long. It was cut into 3 pieces. The length of the first piece of rope was $\frac{1}{5}$ of the original length. The second piece of rope was 0.12 meter longer than the third piece. How long was the second piece of rope?

Solve. Show your work.

23.   A group of 5 friends had dinner at a restaurant. The meal cost $120. There was a 7% tax on the cost of the meal. The group paid a tip that was 15% of the cost of the meal.

a.   How much was the tax?

b.   How much was the tip?

c.   The 5 friends shared the total cost of the meal equally among themselves. How much did each of them have to pay?

Bonus Questions

Solve. Show your work.

1. The volume of 12 pails is the same as the volume of 9 bottles. The total volume of 3 bottles and 5 pails is 21.6 liters. What is the volume of 1 pail?

2. On a test, Pauline answered all 5 questions. She spent 40% of the total time allowed answering the first 2 questions, and 50% of the total time allowed answering the next 2 questions. She found that she had only 6 minutes left for the last question. Pauline had wanted to spend an equal amount of time on each question. How much time should she have spent on each question?

Graphs and Probability

Vocabulary

Fill in the blanks.
Use the words in the box.

1.   The average of a set of data is the

      _____.

2.   Data may be recorded in a _____

      or a _____.

3.   A _____ has vertical and
      horizontal axes.

4.   The _____ of getting a favorable outcome
      can be written as a fraction.

5.   When the probability of an outcome is close to 1,

      the _____ the outcome is to occur.

6.   This spinner is divided into 6 equal parts.

      It is _____ to land on 10.

> more likely
> graph
> mean
> probability
> impossible
> table
> tally chart

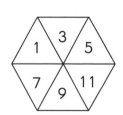

Concepts and Skills

Complete.

7. The scouts sold boxes of cookies to raise money for charity.
The table shows the number of boxes they sold in 6 days.

Day	Number of Boxes
Monday	24
Tuesday	36
Wednesday	19
Thursday	15
Friday	32
Saturday	48

a. Complete the bar graph. Use the data in the table.

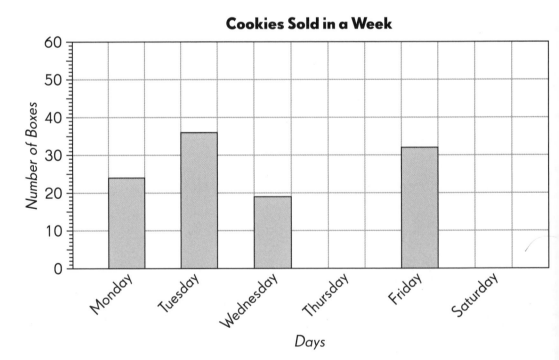

Cookies Sold in a Week

b. On which day was the greatest number of boxes of cookies sold?

_____

8. These are the masses of 4 objects.

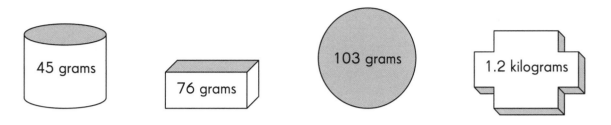

45 grams

76 grams

103 grams

1.2 kilograms

Find the average mass.

Fill in the blanks with *more likely, less likely, equally likely, certain,* or *impossible.*

9. A spinner is divided into 8 equal parts. Each part is labeled as shown.

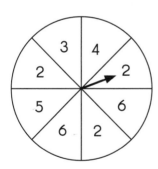

a. It is _____ that the spinner will land on 2.

b. It is _____ that the spinner will land on 7.

c. It is _____ that the spinner will land on 2, 3, 4, 5, or 6.

d. It is _____ that the spinner will land on 3.

Look at the spinner below. Express each probability as a fraction in simplest form.

10.

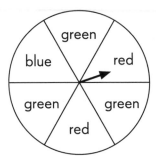

a. The probability of landing on blue is ⬚/⬚.

b. The probability of landing on red is ⬚/⬚.

c. The probability of landing on green is ⬚/⬚.

Problem Solving

Complete. Use the data in the graph.

11.   The graph shows the number of quarters Bob saved every week for 4 weeks.

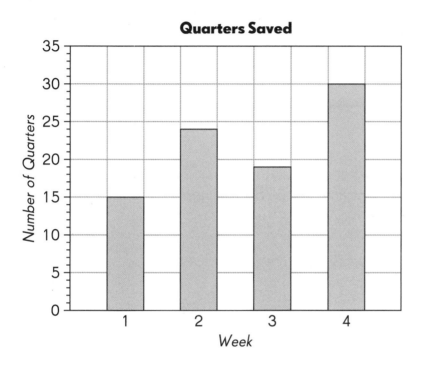

a.   How many quarters did Bob save in Week 3?

b.   How many more quarters did he save in Week 2 than in Week 1?

c.   What is the total number of quarters Bob saved in 4 weeks?

d. How much money did Bob save?

e. What is the average amount of money he saved per week?

12. The mean amount of water in 5 containers is 620 milliliters. The total amount of water in 4 of the containers is 2,750 milliliters. What is the amount of water in the fifth container?

Name: _____   **Date:** _____

TEST PREP

(11) Graphs and Probability

25

Suggested Time:
30 min

Multiple Choice (5 × 2 points = 10 points)

Fill in the circle next to the correct answer.

Use the data in the graph to answer questions 1 and 2.

The graph shows the number of adult and teenage customers who visited a shop from Monday through Thursday.

Customers at a Shop

1.   On which 2 days were there the same number of customers?

    (A) Monday and Tuesday   (B) Wednesday and Thursday

    (C) Monday and Thursday   (D) Tuesday and Thursday

2.   On which day was there the largest difference between the numbers of adult and teenage customers?

    (A) Monday   (B) Tuesday

    (C) Wednesday   (D) Thursday

3. The graph shows the cost of various lengths of wire.

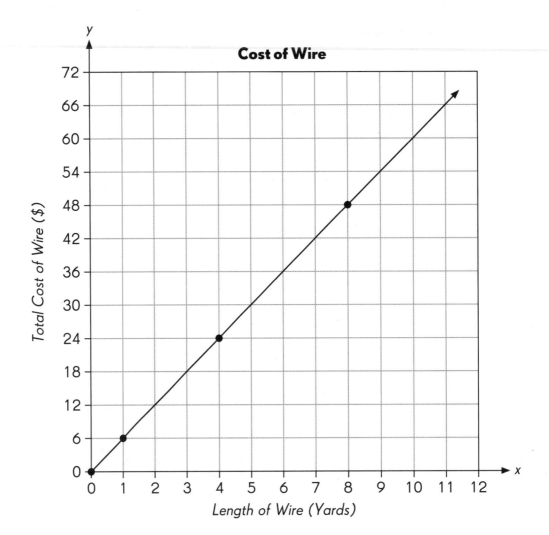

What is the cost of 9 yards of wire?

(A) $54   (B) $60   (C) $66   (D) $70

4. Joe has 4 pairs of shoes: white, black, blue, and brown. He has 2 more pairs of socks than pairs of shoes. Find the number of combinations of pairs of shoes and pairs of socks that Joe can wear.

(A) 5   (B) 6   (C) 15   (D) 24

5. A spinner is divided into 10 equal parts. Each part has a prize labeled on it — a pen, a mug, or a highlighter. The table shows the results of 30 spins.

Pen	Mug	Highlighter
8	15	7

Which is the likely set of prizes on the spinner?

	Pen	Mug	Highlighter	Total Number of Parts
(A)	6	2	2	10
(B)	3	5	2	10
(C)	1	5	4	10
(D)	4	2	4	10

Short Answer   (5 × 2 points = 10 points)

Complete. Use the data in the graph.

6.   George and Henry worked as shop assistants during summer vacation. The graph shows the amount of money George and Henry made in 3 weeks.

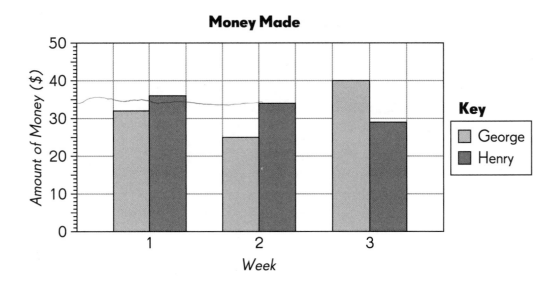

a.   Who made more money in the 3 weeks?

b.   How much more money did he make?

Plot the ordered pairs on the coordinate grid.

7.   (4, 2) and (8, 10)

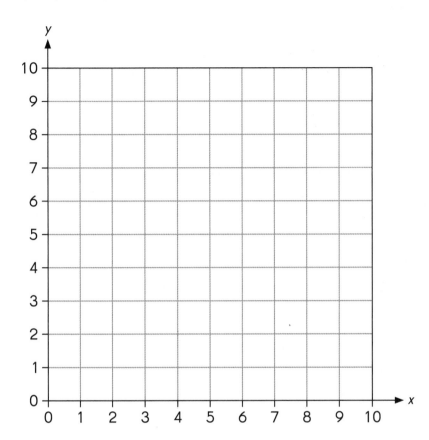

Name: _____ **Date:** _____

Complete. Use the data in the graph.

8. The graph shows the cost of various lengths of curtain fabric.

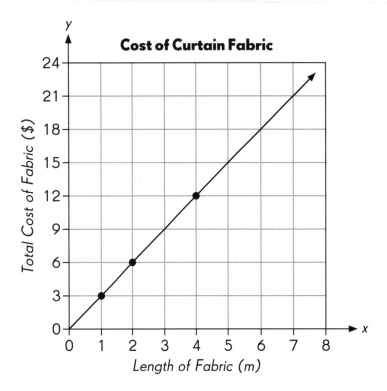

How many meters of curtain fabric can you buy with $21?

Complete.

9. A shop sells ice cream in 3 flavors: strawberry, chocolate, and vanilla. The shop offers 2 toppings: peanuts and raisins. Draw a tree diagram to find the number of combinations the shop can offer.

Solve.

10. A bag contains 5 white balls, 3 green balls and 4 black balls. A ball is drawn from the bag 50 times. The ball is put back in the bag after its color is recorded. The table shows the number of times each color was drawn.

Color	Number of Times Drawn
White	15
Green	26
Black	?

a. What is the experimental probability of drawing a black ball?

b. What is the difference between the theoretical probability and experimental probability of drawing a green ball?

Extended Response   (Question 11: 2 points, Question 12: 3 points)

Solve. Show your work.

11. The graph shows the conversion between feet and yards.

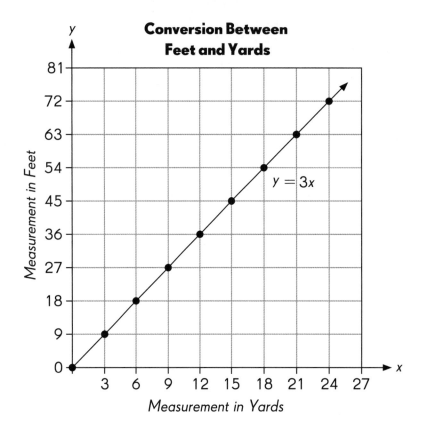

A rectangular plot of land measures 45 feet by 72 feet. Find the area of the land measured in square yards.

12. At a restaurant, the meat choices are roast turkey, fried chicken, and beef steak. The vegetable choices are long beans, salad, and broccoli.

    a. Ms. Spencer wants to order 1 meat dish and 1 vegetable dish. Draw a tree diagram to find the number of combinations she can choose from.

    b. If grilled fish is also available, how many combinations can Ms. Spencer choose from?

Angles

Vocabulary

Fill in the blanks.
Use the words in the box.

1.

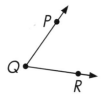

The diagram shows a _____

and X and Y are _____ on it.

angle
rays
line
points
line segment
right angle
perpendicular lines

2.

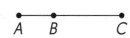

$\overline{AB}$ is a _____.

3.

$\overrightarrow{QP}$ and $\overrightarrow{QR}$ are _____ and an _____ is
formed when they meet at an endpoint.

4.   When two lines meet at a right angle, they are _____.

5.   A _____ measures 90°.

Concepts and Skills

Complete.

6.

_U_ and _V_ are _____ on _____ UV.

7.

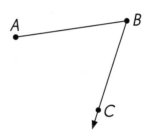

$\overline{AB}$ is a _____ and $\overrightarrow{BC}$ is a _____.

8.

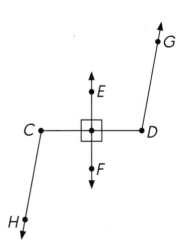

_____ are perpendicular line segments.

9.

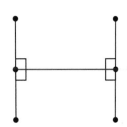

    a. There are _____ right angles in the figure.

    b. The sum of the angle measures of these right angles is

    _____.

10. Mark two angles in the figure.

Name the marked angles.

11.

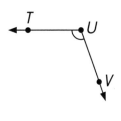

_____

12.

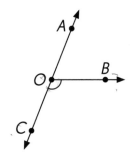

_____

Use a protractor to measure the marked angles.

13.

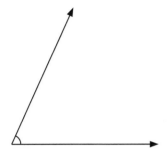

14.

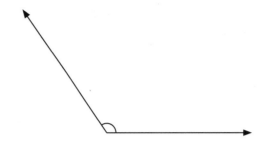

Problem Solving

Find the unknown angle measure.

15.

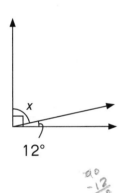

x

12°

$$\begin{array}{r} 90 \\ -12 \\ \hline 78 \end{array}$$

16.

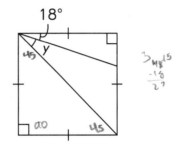

18°

y

45

90

45

$$\begin{array}{r} 3\!\!_{45}^{45} \\ -18 \\ \hline 27 \end{array}$$

12 Angles

TEST PREP

25

Suggested Time: 30 min

Multiple Choice   (5 × 2 points = 10 points)

Fill in the circle next to the correct answer.

1. $\overleftrightarrow{AC}$ is a line. Find the measure of $\angle a$.

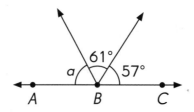

(A) 62°   (B) 118°   (C) 119°   (D) 123°

2.   Find the unknown angle measure.

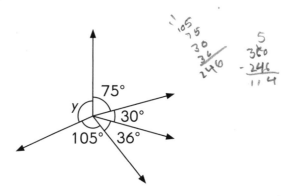

(A) 105°   (B) 114°   (C) 144°   (D) 180°

3. $\overleftrightarrow{AB}$ and $\overleftrightarrow{CD}$ meet at O. Find the measure of $\angle p$.

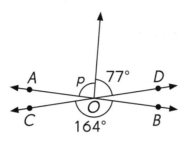

(A) 13°   (B) 16°   (C) 87°   (D) 103°

4. $\overleftrightarrow{AB}$, $\overleftrightarrow{CD}$, and $\overleftrightarrow{EF}$ meet at O. Find the sum of the measures of $\angle s$ and $\angle t$.

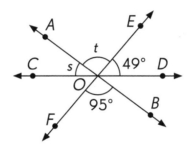

(A) 36°   (B) 85°   (C) 95°   (D) 131°

5. PQRS is a rectangle. $\angle RQT = \angle PTU$. Find the measure of $\angle UTQ$.

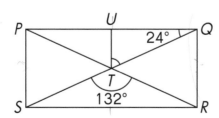

(A) 24°   (B) 48°   (C) 66°   (D) 156°

Short Answer   (5 × 2 points = 10 points)

Find the unknown angle measures.

6. $\overleftrightarrow{AB}$ is a line.

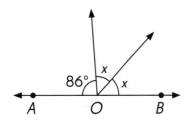

7.   Find the measure of $\angle p$.

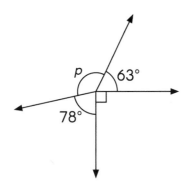

8. $\overleftrightarrow{XY}$ and $\overleftrightarrow{PQ}$ meet at O.

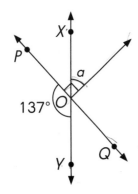

9. In the figure, *ABCD* is a square, and $\overrightarrow{DE}$ and $\overrightarrow{AF}$ are rays.
Find the measure of ∠*EBF*.

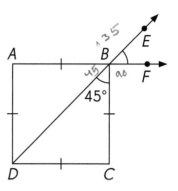

10. Find the measure of ∠*p*.

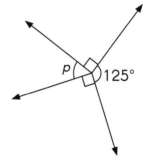

Extended Response

(Question 11: 2 points, Question 12: 3 points)

Solve. Show your work.

11. In the figure, $\overleftrightarrow{AB}$ and $\overleftrightarrow{CD}$ meet at O. Find the sum of the measures of $\angle p$, $\angle q$, and $\angle r$.

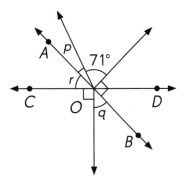

12. $ABCD$ is a square. $\overleftrightarrow{DE}$ and $\overleftrightarrow{FG}$ meet at B. $\angle CBG$ and $\angle GBH$ have equal measures, and $\angle ABD = 45°$. Find the measure of $\angle FBE$.

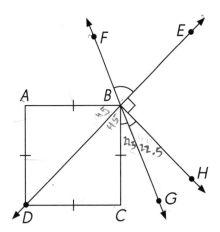

Properties of Triangles and Four-sided Figures

Vocabulary

**Fill in the blanks.
Use the words in the box.**

1. A _____ is a closed figure formed by joining line segments.

2. Polygons have _____ and sides.

3. _____ have 3 sides.

4. Squares, rectangles, and rhombuses are

   examples of _____.

5. One set of opposite sides of a _____ is parallel.

6. When expressions are not equal, they form an _____.

> trapezoid
>
> vertices
>
> quadrilaterals
>
> inequality
>
> polygon
>
> triangles

Concepts and Skills

Write the name of each polygon.

7.

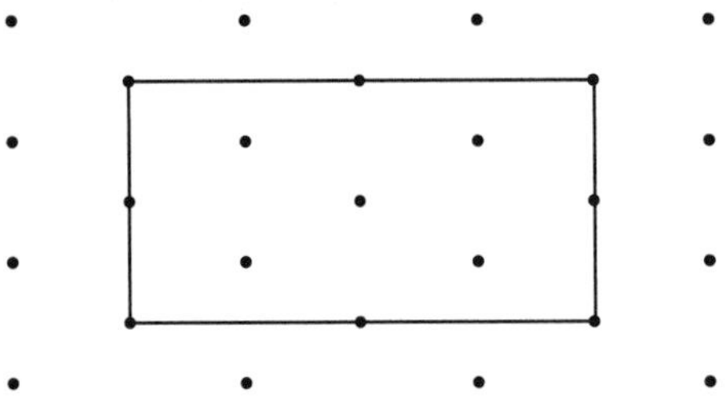

a. 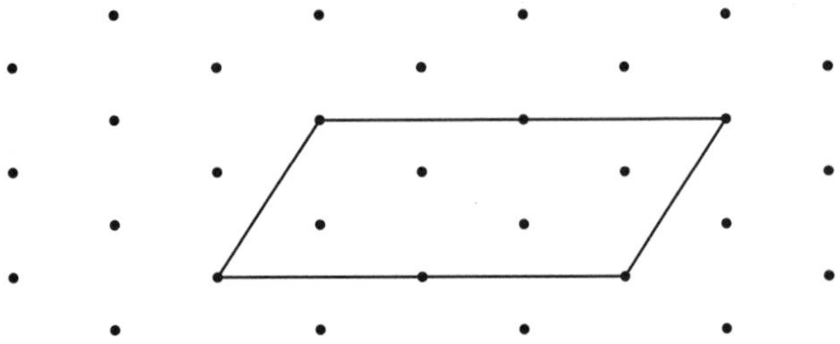 _____   b. _____

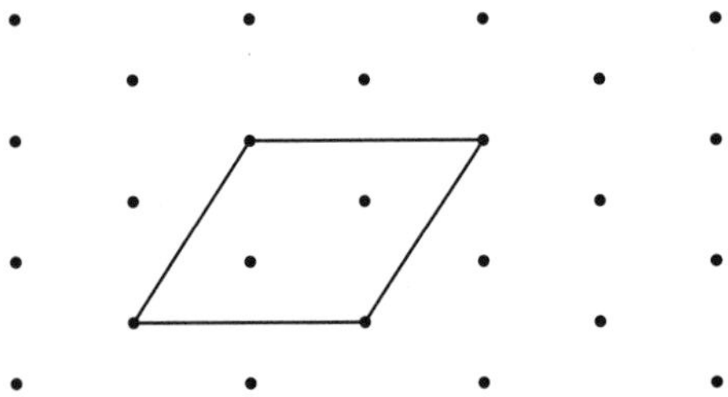

c. 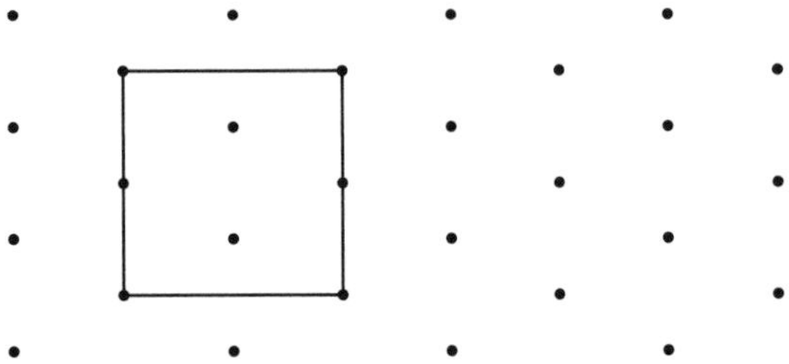 _____   d. _____

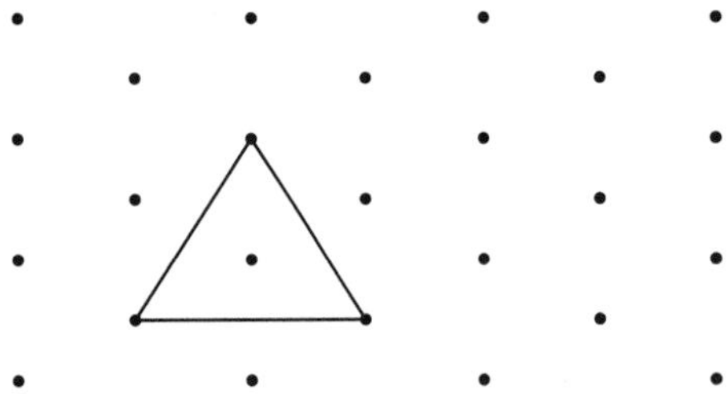

e. 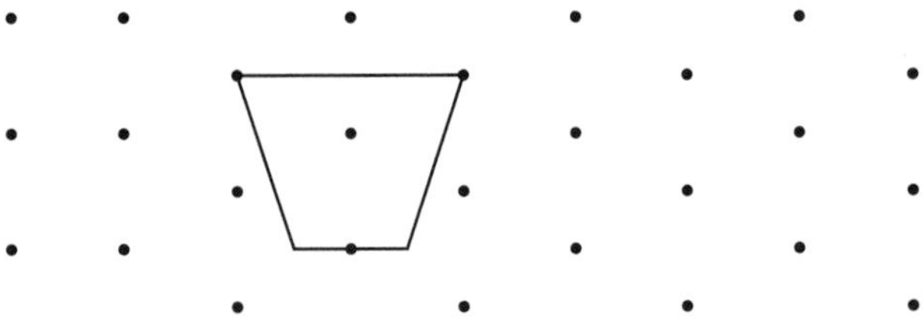 _____   f. _____

Complete.

8.   A triangle has _____ sides.

9.   All four sides of a square are of _____ length.

10. The opposite sides of a square, a rectangle, a parallelogram,

and a rhombus are _____.

11. The _____ sides of a rectangle are of equal length.

12. Only _____ pair of opposite sides of a trapezoid is parallel.

13. ">" means _____ and "<" means _____.

Complete.

14. $\overleftrightarrow{AB}$ and $\overleftrightarrow{CD}$ meet at O.

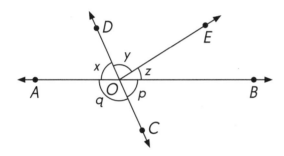

   a. $m\angle$_____ $+ m\angle$_____ $= 180°$

   b. $m\angle x + m\angle$_____ $+ m\angle$_____ $= 180°$

   c. $m\angle p + m\angle$_____ $+ m\angle$_____ $= 180°$

Complete with <, >, or =.

15. If $p = 10$, then $p - 3$ ◯ 8.

16. If $m = 3$, then $25 + m$ ◯ 28.

17. If $y = 7$, then $y + 3$ ◯ 5.

Name: ______________________ Date: ______________

Problem Solving

Solve.

18.

I have 4 equal sides.
But none of my angles form a right angle.
What shape am I?

____

19.

I have 4 sides.
Only 1 pair of my opposite sides is parallel.
What shape am I?

____

TEST PREP 13 Properties of Triangles and Four-sided Figures

25 Suggested Time: 30 min

Multiple Choice   (5 × 2 points = 10 points)

Fill in the circle next to the correct answer.

The figures in this section are not drawn to scale.

1.   Find the unknown angle measure in the triangle.

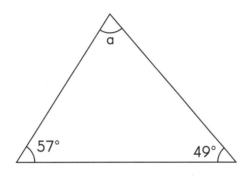

Ⓐ 74°   Ⓑ 106°   Ⓒ 123°   Ⓓ 131°

2.   Find the unknown angle measure in the triangle.

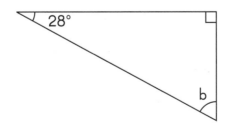

Ⓐ 17°   Ⓑ 62°   Ⓒ 118°   Ⓓ 152°

3.   Triangle *XYZ* is an isosceles triangle. Find the measure of ∠*c*.

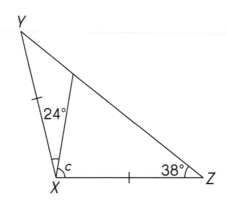

(A) 142°   (B) 120°   (C) 104°   (D) 80°

4.   Which of these sets of side lengths of a triangle is possible?

(A) 4 ft, 9 ft, 5 ft   (B) 5 cm, 5 cm, 10 cm

(C) 6 in., 7 in., 8 in.   (D) 3 m, 6 m, 3 m

5.   Triangle *ABC* is a right triangle and *BCD* is an equilateral triangle.
Find the measure of ∠*DAC*.

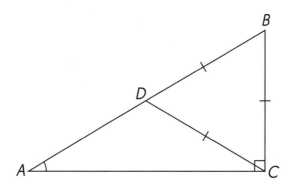

(A) 30°   (B) 60°   (C) 120°   (D) 50°

Short Answer   (5 × 2 points = 10 points)

Write your answer in the space provided.

The figures in this section are not drawn to scale.

6.   *ABC* and *BCD* are triangles. Find the unknown angle measure.

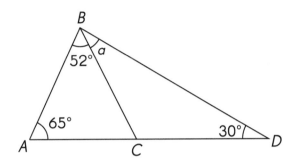

7.   Triangle *ABC* is a right triangle.

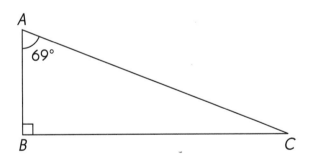

a.   Complete with $<$, $>$, or $=$.

$m\angle BAC \bigcirc m\angle ACB$

b.   What is the difference in the angle measures of $\angle BAC$ and $\angle ACB$?

8. Triangle *ABC* is a right triangle. Triangle *BDE* is an equilateral triangle and Triangle *CDE* is an isosceles triangle. Find the measure of ∠*a*.

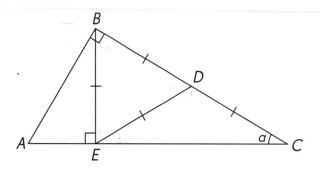

9. *ABCD* is a parallelogram where $\overline{AB} \parallel \overline{DC}$. Triangle *BCE* is an isosceles triangle. Find the measure of ∠*ABE*.

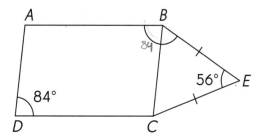

10. *ABCD* is a rhombus. Triangle *ABE* is an isosceles triangle. $\overline{CE}$ is a line segment. Find the measures of $\angle a$ and $\angle b$.

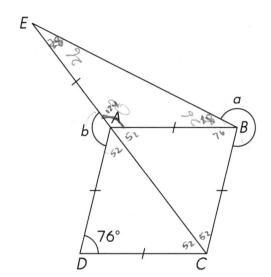

Extended Response   (Question 11: 2 points, Question 12: 3 points)

Solve. Show your work.

11. *ABC* and *EFG* are triangles. Find the sum of the measures of ∠a, ∠b, ∠c, and ∠d.

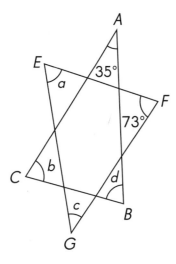

12. *ABCE* is a trapezoid where $\overline{AB} \parallel \overline{EC}$. *ABDE* is a rhombus. Find the measure of ∠*EBC*.

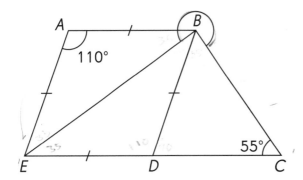

PRE-TEST 14 — Three-Dimensional Shapes

Vocabulary

Fill in the blanks.
Use the words in the box.

1. A _____ is a flat figure made up of line segments, curves, or both.

2. In a polygon, the _____ are formed when two sides meet at a point.

3. A _____ is a plane figure.

4. A _____ is a solid figure.

5. _____ figures have the same shape and size.

vertices
plane figure
congruent
pentagon
pyramid

Concepts and Skills

Write your answer in the space provided.

6. Identify the plane figures and the solid figures.

A   B   C   D   E   F

The plane figures are _____.

The solid figures are _____.

7.   Name the parts of the polygon.

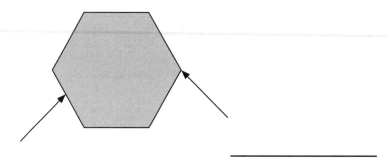

_____   _____

8.   Name a solid which has only a curved surface.   _____

9.   Name a solid which has 1 flat surface and 1 curved surface.

_____

10.   Name a solid which has only flat surfaces.

_____

11.   Look at the figure. Name a pair of parallel line segments.

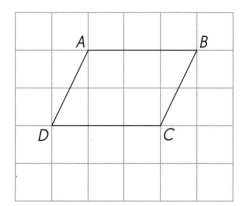

_____

12. Trace the figures. Then identify the pairs of congruent figures.

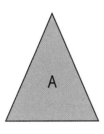

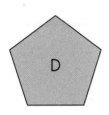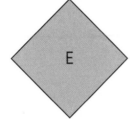

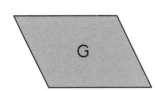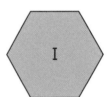

 **TEST PREP 14** # Three-Dimensional Shapes

25

Suggested Time: 30 min

Multiple Choice   (5 × 2 points = 10 points)

Fill in the circle next to the correct answer.

1.   Name the solid.

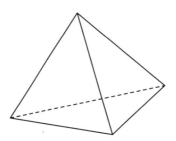

(A) triangular prism   (B) triangular pyramid

(C) square pyramid   (D) rectangular prism

2.   How many faces and vertices does the solid have?

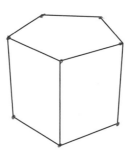

(A) 5 faces, 5 vertices   (B) 5 faces, 7 vertices

(C) 7 faces, 10 vertices   (D) 5 faces, 10 vertices

3.   Which net would form a rectangular prism?

(A)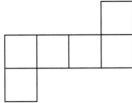

(B)

(C)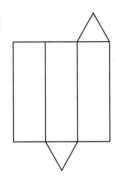

(D)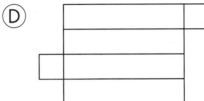

4.   Which solid does **not** have flat surfaces?

(A) cone   (B) cylinder   (C) cube   (D) sphere

5.   The solid is cut vertically along the line shown. Name one of the solids that is formed.

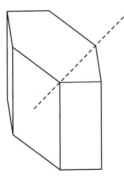

(A) triangular prism   (B) rectangular pyramid

(C) triangular pyramid   (D) rectangular prism

Short Answer   (5 × 2 points = 10 points)

Write your answer in the space provided.

6.   Name the solid.

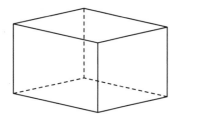

_____

7.   Name the parts of the solid.

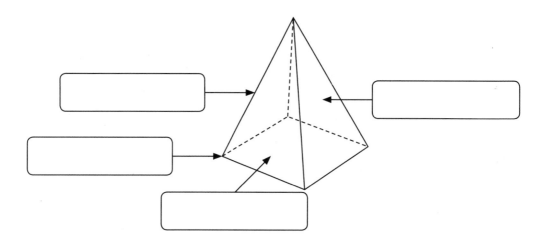

8.   Explain why this figure is not a pyramid.

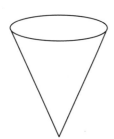

_____

_____

Complete.

9.   The solid figure is a pentagonal pyramid.

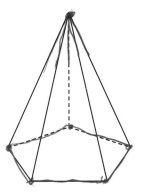

    a.   How many edges and vertices does a pentagonal pyramid have?

    _____

    b.   Name the shapes of the base and the faces.

    _____

10.   Draw a net for the cylinder.

Extended Response   (Question 11: 2 points, Question 12: 3 points)

Solve.

11.   Which two of these nets can form a cube? Fill in the circles next to the correct answers.

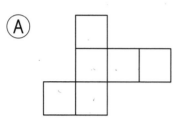

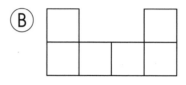

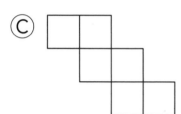

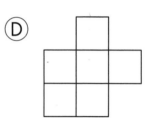

12.   Draw the missing face to show the net of a pyramid. Then identify the type of pyramid that can be formed from this net.

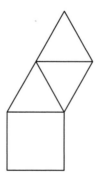

The type of pyramid that can be formed is a _____.

PRE-TEST

Surface Area and Volume

Vocabulary

Fill in the blanks.
Use the words in the box.

1.   A cube has 6 faces. Each face is a

      _____.

2.   A _____ is a solid figure with
      two parallel and congruent bases joined by
      rectangular faces.

3.   The base of a _____ is a triangle.

4.   The _____ is the amount of space
      an object occupies.

5.   The _____ is the maximum amount of liquid a container can
      hold.

6.   The _____ of a square, a rectangle, and a triangle can be

      found by using _____.

prism
triangular prism
formulas
capacity
area
volume
square

Concepts and Skills

Identify each figure.

7.

8.

9.

_____   _____   _____

Complete.

10.

a. What is the volume of the juice in the jug?

_____

b. What is the capacity of the jug?

_____

Solve.

11. The capacity of a fish tank is 30 liters. $\frac{2}{3}$ of the tank is filled with water. Find the volume of the water in the tank.

Problem Solving

Solve. Show your work.

12.   Look at the floor plan for an apartment. The bathroom floor is in the shape
of a square. What is the total area of the floor of the apartment?

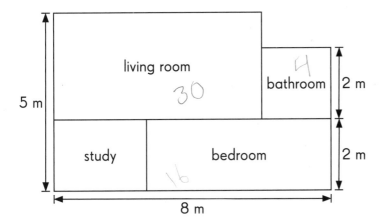

living room

30

5 m

bathroom   4   2 m

study   bedroom   2 m

16

8 m

Surface Area and Volume

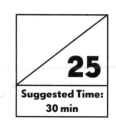

25

Suggested Time:
30 min

Multiple Choice (5 × 2 points = 10 points)

Fill in the circle next to the correct answer.

1. How many cubes are used to build the solid?

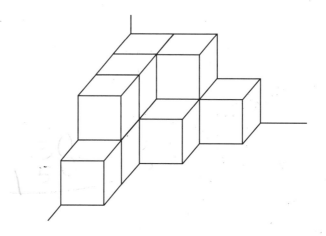

  Ⓐ 9   Ⓑ 10   Ⓒ 11   Ⓓ 12

2. Find the total surface area of the outside of the tank. It has an open top.

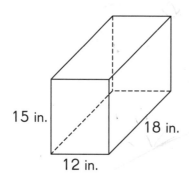

15 in.

18 in.

12 in.

  Ⓐ 180 in.²   Ⓑ 666 in.²

  Ⓒ 1,116 in.²   Ⓓ 1,332 in.²

3. Which of these has edges that are 3 times as long as a unit cube?

Ⓐ

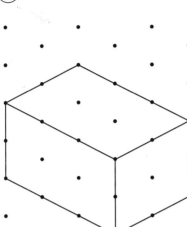

Ⓑ

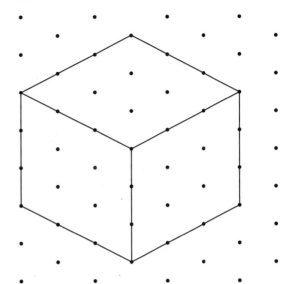

Ⓒ

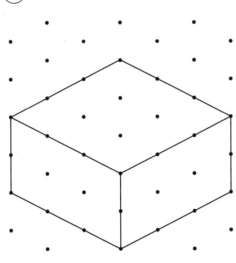

Ⓓ

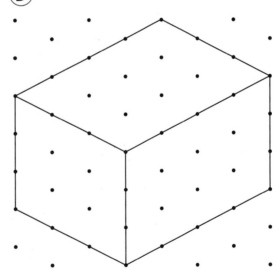

4. The solid is made up of cubes that have edges that measure 2 centimeters. What is the volume of the solid?

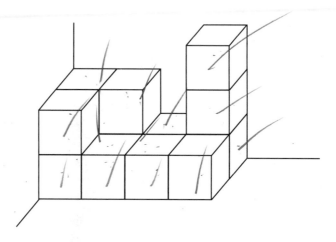

(A) 11 cm^3

(B) 13 cm^3

(C) 88 cm^3

(D) 104 cm^3

5. A tank has water in it at a height of 7 centimeters. How much more water is needed to fill the tank to the brim?

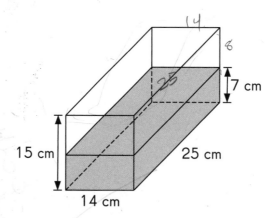

(A) 2.45 L

(B) 2.8 L

(C) 5.25 L

(D) 6.1 L

Short Answer   (5 × 2 points = 10 points)

Write your answer in the space provided.

6. How many cubes are used to build the solid?

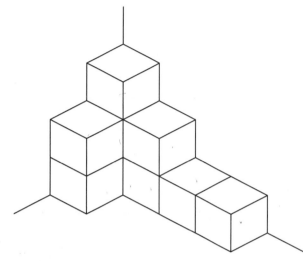

_____ cubes are used to build the solid.

7. Draw the different views of a rectangular prism that is made up of 3 unit cubes.

Complete.

8. Find the total surface area of the triangular prism.

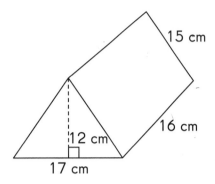

9. The length of a rectangular block of wood is twice its width. The width of the block of wood is 12 inches. Find the volume of the block of wood.

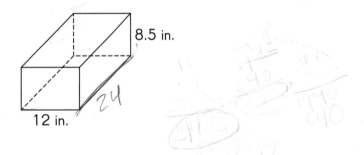

10. A rectangular container has sides that measure 9 centimeters by 12 centimeters by 23 centimeters. Joan filled the container to its brim with water. How much water must she pour out of the container so that only $\frac{2}{3}$ of the volume of water is left in the container? Give your answer in milliliters.

Extended Response   (Question 11: 2 points, Question 12: 3 points)

Solve. Show your work.

11. A tank is $\frac{3}{4}$-filled with water. Water from the tank is used to fill smaller containers. Each small container has a square base with edges that measure 16 centimeters each, and a height of 5 centimeters. How many small containers can the water from the tank fill?

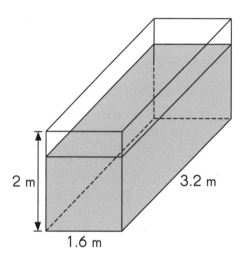
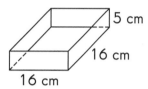

Solve. Show your work.

12. A tank measures 30 centimeters by 30 centimeters by 50 centimeters. It is filled with water from a tap that flows at a rate of 6 liters per minute. How long would it take to fill $\frac{4}{5}$ of the tank with water? Give your answer in minutes and seconds.

Focus Lessons Assessments

Whole Number Multiplication and Division

Multiply.

1. $249 \times 10^2 = $ _____

2. $1{,}850 \times 10^2 = $ _____

3. $320 \times 10^3 = $ _____

4. $5{,}700 \times 10^3 = $ _____

Simplify. Show your work.

5. $144 \div [16 \div (4 \times 2)]$

6. $48 \div \{12 \div [(6 - 2) \times 3]\}$

7. $\{969 - [27 - (29 + 43) \div 4]\} \div 3$

8. $9 \times \{109 - [(36 \times 4) + 75] \div 3\}$

Multiplying and Dividing Fractions and Mixed Numbers

Divide. You may draw models to help you.

1. $7 \div \dfrac{1}{8}$

2. $5 \div \dfrac{1}{6}$

3. $9 \div \dfrac{1}{7}$

4. $8 \div \dfrac{1}{4}$

Solve. Show your work.

5. George uses $\dfrac{1}{9}$ of a small can of strawberry jam to make a sandwich. How many sandwiches can he make with 5 cans of strawberry jam?

6. Sandra buys 6 pounds of cherries to make individual mini-pies. If she uses $\frac{1}{5}$ pound of cherries for each pie, how many pies can she make?

7. Carter has 9 pounds of sand to put in fish tanks. He uses 5 pounds of sand for a large fish tank and puts the rest equally in the small fish tanks. If he puts $\frac{1}{3}$ pound of sand in each small fish tank, how many fish tanks does he put sand into?

8. Olivia has 7 cups of blackberries. She uses 3 cups of blackberries to make a cake and uses the rest to make blackberry tarts. If she uses $\frac{1}{8}$ cup of blackberries for each tart, how many blackberry tarts does she make?

6 Area of a Triangle

Find the area of each figure.

1.

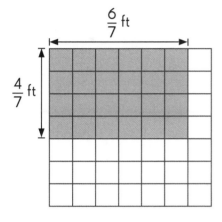

$\frac{6}{7}$ ft

$\frac{4}{7}$ ft

2.

$\frac{2}{5}$ yd

$\frac{3}{5}$ yd

3.

$\frac{3}{4}$ ft

$\frac{3}{8}$ ft

4.

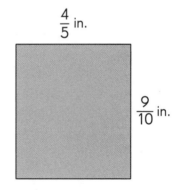

$\frac{4}{5}$ in.

$\frac{9}{10}$ in.

CHAPTER 9 Multiplying and Dividing Decimals

Multiply.

1. $0.39 \times 10^2 =$ _____

2. $2.504 \times 10^2 =$ _____

3. $1.826 \times 10^3 =$ _____

4. $9.75 \times 10^3 =$ _____

11 Graphs and Probability

Sue measured the amount of water in 15 tanks. She recorded her data in the table below.

Volume of Water in Tanks

Volume (gal)	$\frac{1}{8}$	$\frac{1}{4}$	$\frac{3}{8}$	$\frac{1}{2}$	$\frac{5}{8}$	$\frac{3}{4}$
Number of Tanks	1	3	2	5	1	3

Make a line plot to show the data in the table.

1.

Use the data in the line plot to answer questions 2 and 3.

2. What is the total amount of water in the 15 tanks?

3. If all the water in the 15 tanks is redistributed equally among the tanks, how much water is in each tank?

CHAPTER 15

Surface Area and Volume

Find the volume of each rectangular prism.

1.

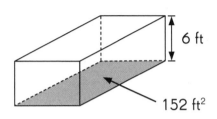

6 ft

152 ft²

2.

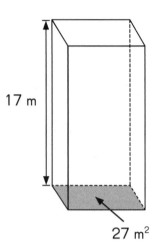

17 m

27 m²

Volume = _____   Volume = _____

Solve.

3.   A drawer is shaped like a rectangular prism.
It has a height of 8 inches and the area of its base is 284 square inches.
Find the volume of the drawer.

4. A rectangular cereal box has a base of 189 square centimeters, and a height of 32 centimeters. Find the volume of the box.

Find the volume of each solid that is composed of two rectangular prism.

5.

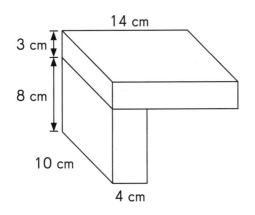

14 cm

3 cm

8 cm

10 cm

4 cm

6.

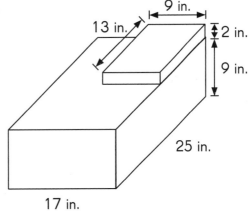

9 in.

13 in.

2 in.

9 in.

25 in.

17 in.

Volume = _____   Volume = _____

Solve.

7. A rectangular bench is made up of a wooden block and a cushion as shown. Find the volume of the bench.

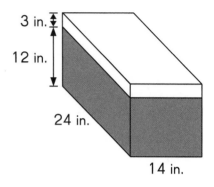

3 in.

12 in.

24 in.

14 in.

8. A bakery has a two-tier rectangular pastry display case in the diagram as shown. Find the total volume of the pastry display case.

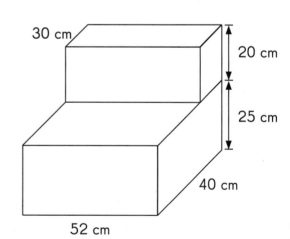

30 cm

20 cm

25 cm

40 cm

52 cm

End-of-Year Test

Multiple Choice (10 × 2 points = 20 points)

50

**Suggested Time:
45 min**

Fill in the circle next to the correct answer.

1. Estimate 5,642 × 3 using front-end estimation.

(A) 12,000   (B) 15,000

(C) 16,800   (D) 18,000

2. What number belongs in the box?

$90 \div (15 - 13) + 6 = \boxed{}$

(A) 1   (B) 45   (C) 48   (D) 51

3. Of the 250 people at a concert, 160 are men. Half of the rest of the people are children. What percent of the people are women?

(A) 9%   (B) 16%   (C) 18%   (D) 36%

4. In a race, a triathlete runs $\frac{1}{3}$ of the total distance, cycles $\frac{2}{5}$ of the total distance, and swims the remaining distance. He swims 1,200 meters. What is the total distance of the race?

(A) 3,600 meters   (B) 4,500 meters

(C) 6,000 meters   (D) 7,200 meters

5. 5 boys made *s* doughnuts. They sold the doughnuts for $3 each and shared the money they made equally. How much money did each boy get?

(A) $\$\frac{3s}{5}$ (B) $\$\frac{5s}{3}$ (C) $\$\frac{5 + s}{5}$ (D) $\$15s$

6. Find the area of the shaded part of the figure.

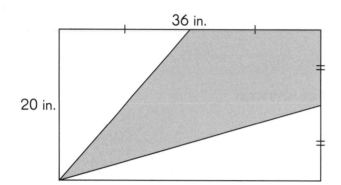

Ⓐ 112 square inches

Ⓑ 180 square inches

Ⓒ 360 square inches

Ⓓ 720 square inches

7. The graph shows the number of foreign stamps and local stamps 3 students collected.

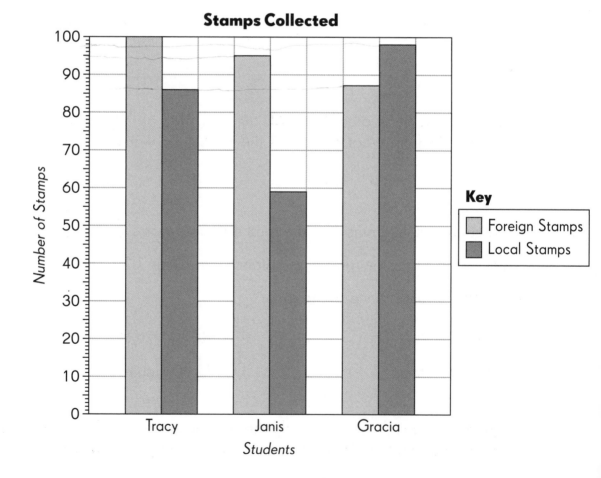

How many more foreign stamps than local stamps are there?

Ⓐ 39   Ⓑ 243   Ⓒ 283   Ⓓ 525

8. $\overleftrightarrow{AB}$ and $\overleftrightarrow{CD}$ meet at O. Find the measure of $\angle a$. The figure is not drawn to scale.

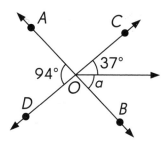

 A 143°   **B** 131°   **C** 86°   **D** 57°

9. Which solid has 4 rectangular faces and 2 square faces?

A
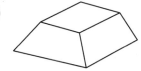

B

C
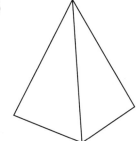

D

10. A tank that measures 40 feet by 36 feet by 18 feet is filled with water to $\frac{5}{6}$ of its height. $\frac{1}{3}$ of the water is poured out of the tank. How much water is left in the tank?

A 25,920 ft³

B 21,600 ft³

C 14,400 ft³

D 7,200 ft³

Short Answer (10 × 2 points = 20 points)

Write your answer in the space provided.

11. Multiply 687 by 98.

12. Divide 6.42 by 5. Round your answer to the nearest hundredth.

13. Find $6\frac{1}{4} + 2\frac{7}{9} + 1\frac{3}{4}$.

Solve.

14. Mr. Abdul buys 4 bags of charcoal for a barbeque party. Each bag weighs $5\frac{1}{2}$ pounds. What is the total weight of the charcoal?

15. Simplify $16f - 3f + 9 + f - 7$.

Solve. Use models to help you.

16. The ratio of the number of red beads to the number of green beads to the number of blue beads is 2 : 3 : 7. There are 150 more blue beads than red beads. How many beads are there in all?

Solve. Show your work.

17. There are 3 different cameras and 5 different books. A teacher wants to give 1 camera and 1 book to a student. Find the number of combinations the teacher can choose from.

18. In the figure, *ABCD* is a parallelogram. Find the measure of ∠*DEA*.

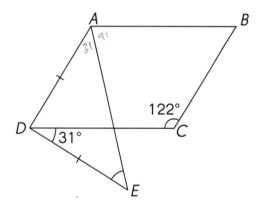

Solve.

19. Name the shape that the net will form.

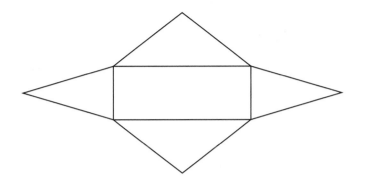

_____

20. The solid is made up of 2 rectangular prisms, A and B. Solid A is painted red. Find the total surface area of solid A that is painted red.

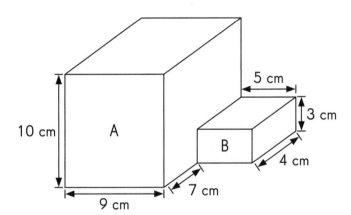

Name: _____ **Date:** _____

Solve. Show your work.

21. Pritz made $7\frac{2}{3}$ pints of pineapple juice. She drank $\frac{5}{6}$ pints of the juice, and poured $\frac{3}{4}$ of the remaining juice equally into 3 bottles. How much pineapple juice does each bottle contain?

22. The rectangular tank shown is filled with water to $\frac{4}{5}$ of its height. The water is then poured into the cubical tank until the cubical tank is half full. How much water is left in the rectangular tank? Give your answer in liters. (1 L = 1,000 cm³)

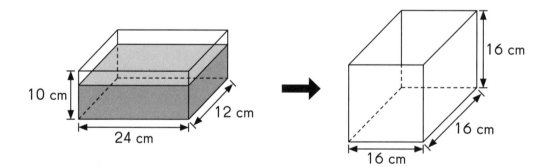

Solve. Show your work.

23. A baker made cakes, cookies, and buns. Of the total number of baked products he made, 28% were cookies. The number of cakes was 3 times the number of buns. He made 270 cakes. He sold 40 buns and 120 cakes. How many cookies must he sell so that the ratio of the number of buns left to the number of cakes left to the number of cookies left is 1 : 3 : 2?

Bonus Questions

Solve. Show your work.

1.   Paul has just enough money to buy either 5 erasers and 30 pencils or
10 erasers and 24 pencils. Each eraser costs $0.30. How much does each
pencil cost?

2.   All the triangles in the following figures are equilateral triangles. In figure 2,
a smaller triangle is formed inside the triangle in figure 1 by connecting
the midpoints of the sides of the bigger triangle. Figure 3 and figure 4 are
obtained in the same way. The area of the biggest equilateral triangle is
128 cm². Find the area of the smallest equilateral triangle in figure 4.

Figure 1   Figure 2   Figure 3   Figure 4

Answers

1. value
2. compare
3. rounding
4. front-end estimation
5. fifteen thousand, seven hundred thirty-two
6. 60,000
7. a. 40,000   b. 400,000
8. a. $76,480 = 70,000 + \underline{6,000} + 400 + \underline{80}$
   b. $620,315 = \underline{600,000} + \underline{20,000} + 300 + 10 + 5$
9. a. >   b. <
10. 374,875   374,248   355,410
11. a. 37,900   b. 56,400
12. $4,000 + 7,000 = 11,000$
13. $10,000 - 3,000 = 7,000$
14. $500 + 800 = 1,300$
15. $900 - 400 = 500$
16. 2,742 rounds to 3,000.
    $3,000 \times 7 = 21,000$
    $2,742 \times 7$ is about 21,000.
17. $700 \times 9 = 6,300$
    $800 \times 9 = 7,200$
    6,502 is nearer to 6,300 than to 7,200.
    $6,300 \div 9 = 700$
    $6,502 \div 9$ is about 700.
18. a. Ms. Carlson has more money.
    b. $\$7,145 \rightarrow \$7,100$
       $\$3,799 \rightarrow \$3,800$
       They have about $\$7,100 + \$3,800 = \$10,900$.
19. $315 \text{ ft} \rightarrow 300 \text{ ft}$
    $175 \text{ ft} \rightarrow 100 \text{ ft}$
    $300 \text{ ft} \times 100 \text{ ft} = 30,000 \text{ sq. ft}$
    The area of the rectangular field is about 30,000 square feet.

1. C   2. B   3. D   4. C
5. C
6. a. six million, three hundred twenty-six thousand, five hundred eight
   b. $4,781,020 = \underline{4,000,000} + 700,000 + 80,000 + 1,000 + \underline{20}$
7. a. <   b. >

8. $2,691 \rightarrow 2,000$
   $8,173 \rightarrow 8,000$
   $4,724 \rightarrow 4,000$
   $2,000 + 8,000 + 4,000 = 14,000$
   $691 + 173 + 724 \rightarrow 600 + 100 + 700$
                          $= 1,400$
   1,400 rounded to the nearest thousand is 1,000.
   $14,000 + 1,000 = 15,000$
   The estimated sum is 15,000.
9. $7,685 \rightarrow 7,000$
   $3,768 \rightarrow 3,000$
   $7,000 - 3,000 = 4,000$
   $768 - 685 \rightarrow 700 - 600 = 100$
   100 rounded to the nearest thousand is 0.
   $4,000 - 0 = 4,000$
   The estimated difference is 4,000.
10. 3,937,245; 4,937,445
    Rule: Count on by 500,100.
11. $6,157 \rightarrow 6,000$
    $6,000 \times 9 = 54,000$
    There are about 54,000 passengers in total.
12. $3,548 \rightarrow 3,200$
    $3,200 \div 8 = 400$
    Each crate has about 400 mangoes.
    or $3,548 \rightarrow 4,000$
    $4,000 \div 8 = 500$
    Each crate has about 500 mangoes.

1. expanded form
2. multiplication facts
3. product
4. bar model
5. nearest 1,000
6. a. eight million, two hundred thirty-eight thousand, six hundred fifteen
   b. $8,000,000 + 200,000 + 30,000 + 8,000 + 600 + 10 + 5$
7. $? = 315 + 89 = 404$
8. $? = 8,614 - 509 = 8,105$
9. $? = 8 \times 15 = 120$
10. $? = 294 \div 7 = 42$
11. $? = 156 \div 6 = 26$
12. 8,000   13. 82,000
14. $400 \times 9 = 3,600$
15. $800 \times 7 = 5,600$
16. $900 \times 5 = 4,500$
17. $200 \times 8 = 1,600$

18. 4 × 90 = 360
    4 × 100 = 400
    372 is nearer to 360 than to 400.
    360 ÷ 4 = 90
    372 ÷ 4 is about 90.

19. 6 × 30 = 180
    6 × 40 = 240
    197 is nearer to 180 than to 240.
    180 ÷ 6 = 30
    197 ÷ 6 is about 30.

20. 198 ÷ 5 ➞ 200 ÷ 5 = 40
    Each crate has about 40 oranges.

21.
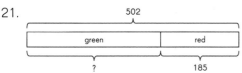

    ? = 502 − 185
      = 317
    There are 317 green beads.

22.

```
        495
┌──┬─────────────────────┬──┐
│ 9│                     │ 9│
└──┴─────────────────────┴──┘
         ? groups
```

    ? = 495 ÷ 9
      = 55
    Hector will need 55 envelopes.

Test Prep 2

1. B   2. C   3. C   4. D

5. A

6. 2,356 × 700 = (2,356 × 7) × 100
                = 16,492 × 100
                = 1,649,200

7.
$$
\begin{array}{r}
\overset{4\ \ \ 1}{\underset{5\ \ \ 1}{8,0\,9\,3}} \\
\times\quad\ \ \ 5\,6 \\
\hline
4\,8,5\,5\,8 \\
4\,0\,4,6\,5\,0 \\
\hline
4\,5\,3,2\,0\,8
\end{array}
$$

8. 1,620 × 68 = 1,600 × 70
              = 1,600 × 7 × 10
              = 11,200 × 10
              = 112,000
   The area of the wall is about 112,000 square
   centimeters.

9. 3,812 ÷ 48 = 4,000 ÷ 50
             = (4,000 ÷ 10) ÷ 5
             = 400 ÷ 5
             = 80
   About 80 rows of seats are occupied.

10. Cost of one camera = ($8,153 + $847) ÷ 100
                       = $9,000 ÷ 100
                       = $90
    $150 − $90 = $60
    Tom earned $60 from selling each camera.

11. $5,645 − $500 = $5,145
    $5,145 ÷ 7 = $735
    He paid $735 each month.

12. a. 1,400 ÷ 35 = 40
       40 × $1.60 = $64
       Jody paid $64 for the beads.
    b. 1,400 ÷ 16 = $87\frac{1}{2}$

       She needs 88 small boxes.

Pre-Test 3

1. like fractions   2. prime numbers
3. equivalent fractions 4. unlike fractions
5. $\frac{3}{10}, \frac{7}{10}$ 6. a. $\frac{3}{5}$ b. $\frac{1}{3}$
7. a. 32   b. 5   8. 23   9. 9
10. $\frac{2}{7}, \frac{1}{3}; \frac{2}{7}, \frac{3}{8}; \frac{2}{7}, \frac{5}{8}; \frac{3}{8}, \frac{1}{3}; \frac{1}{3}, \frac{5}{8}$
11. a.
$$
\begin{array}{r}
5 \\
3\overline{)17} \\
\underline{15} \\
2
\end{array}
$$
    b.
$$
\begin{array}{r}
1 \\
20\overline{)23} \\
\underline{20} \\
3
\end{array}
$$

    $\frac{17}{3} = 5\frac{2}{3}$ $\frac{23}{20} = 1\frac{3}{20}$

12. $\frac{1}{3} + \frac{1}{12} = \frac{4}{12} + \frac{1}{12} = \frac{5}{12}$

13. $\frac{5}{8} + \frac{1}{4} + \frac{1}{2}$

    $= \frac{5}{8} + \frac{2}{8} + \frac{4}{8} = \frac{11}{8} = 1\frac{3}{8}$

14. $\frac{7}{9} - \frac{1}{3} = \frac{7}{9} - \frac{3}{9} = \frac{4}{9}$

15. $3 - \frac{1}{2} - \frac{1}{6} = \frac{18}{6} - \frac{3}{6} - \frac{1}{6}$

    $= \frac{14}{6}$

    $= \frac{7}{3}$

    $= 2\frac{1}{3}$

16. 0.6 17. 0.74

18. $1 - \frac{3}{5} - \frac{1}{10} = \frac{10}{10} - \frac{6}{10} - \frac{1}{10} = \frac{3}{10}$

Linus has $\frac{3}{10}$ of the cake.

19. $\frac{4}{5} + \frac{3}{10} = \frac{8}{10} + \frac{3}{10} = \frac{11}{10} = 1\frac{1}{10}$

He has $1\frac{1}{10}$ kilograms of raisins now.

Test Prep 3

1. D   2. C   3. A   4. C
5. B

6. a. $2\frac{3}{4} + 3\frac{2}{5}$

   $= 2\frac{15}{20} + 3\frac{8}{20}$

   $= 5\frac{23}{20}$

   $= 6\frac{3}{20}$

   b. $3\frac{1}{2} - 1\frac{7}{8}$

   $= 3\frac{4}{8} - 1\frac{7}{8}$

   $= 2\frac{12}{8} - 1\frac{7}{8}$

   $= 1\frac{5}{8}$

7. a. $0 + \frac{1}{2} + \frac{1}{2} = 1$

   b. $1 - \frac{1}{2} = \frac{1}{2}$

8. $\frac{2}{7} + (\frac{2}{7} + \frac{1}{3}) = \frac{19}{21}$

   Gail sold $\frac{19}{21}$ of the cookies on the two days.

9. $(8 - 3) \div 8 = \frac{5}{8}$

   Each shorter piece of ribbon is $\frac{5}{8}$ foot long.

10. $1 - (\frac{3}{7} + \frac{2}{5}) = 1 - \frac{29}{35} = \frac{6}{35}$

    $\frac{6}{35}$ of the land is used to grow tomato plants.

11.

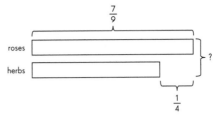

$\frac{7}{9} + (\frac{7}{9} - \frac{1}{4}) = \frac{7}{9} + \frac{19}{36} = \frac{47}{36} = 1\frac{11}{36}$

Jenny uses $1\frac{11}{36}$ gallons of water to water the roses and herbs.

12. Julian poured $3\frac{11}{12} - 1\frac{2}{5} = \frac{47}{12} - \frac{7}{5}$

    $= \frac{151}{60} = 2\frac{31}{60}$ L

    $3\frac{11}{12} + 2\frac{31}{60} = \frac{47}{12} + \frac{151}{60} = \frac{386}{60}$

    $= 6\frac{13}{30}$ L

    $10\ L - 6\frac{13}{30}\ L = 3\frac{17}{30}\ L$

    $3\frac{17}{30}$ liters more water is still needed to fill the tank.

Pre-Test 4

1. simplify   2. improper fraction

3. decimal   4. $\frac{2}{9}; \frac{4}{18}; \frac{6}{27}$

5. $\frac{15}{18} = \frac{15 \div 3}{18 \div 3} = \frac{5}{6}$

6. $\frac{14}{35} = \frac{14 \div 7}{35 \div 7} = \frac{2}{5}$

7. $3 - \frac{3}{10} = \frac{30}{10} - \frac{3}{10} = \frac{27}{10} = 2\frac{7}{10}$

8. a. $\frac{15}{4} = \frac{12}{4} + \frac{3}{4}$

   $= 3 + \frac{3}{4}$

   $= 3\frac{3}{4}$

   b. $\frac{21}{5} = \frac{20}{5} + \frac{1}{5}$

   $= 4 + \frac{1}{5}$

   $= 4\frac{1}{5}$

9. $5\frac{2}{5} = 5 + \frac{2}{5}$

$\qquad = \frac{25}{5} + \frac{2}{5}$

$\qquad = \frac{27}{5}$

10. $\frac{3}{5} = \frac{3 \times 20}{5 \times 20}$

$\qquad = \frac{60}{100}$

$\qquad = 0.6$

11. $\frac{2}{3} \times 36 = \frac{2 \times 36}{3}$

$\qquad\qquad = \frac{72}{3}$

$\qquad\qquad = 24$

12. $25 \times 4 \div (12 - 8) = 25 \times 4 \div 4$

$\qquad\qquad\qquad\qquad = 100 \div 4$

$\qquad\qquad\qquad\qquad = 25$

13.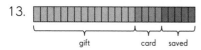

14. 9 cupcakes ➝ $18

$\quad$ 1 cupcake ➝ $18 \div 9 = \$2$

$\quad$ 6 cupcakes ➝ $6 \times \$2 = \$12$

$\quad$ 6 cupcakes cost $12.

15. Teddy bears: $\frac{1}{3} \times 18 = 6$

$\quad$ Balls: $\frac{1}{6} \times 18 = 3$

$\quad$ Dolls: $18 - 6 - 3 = 9$

$\quad$ Kim has 9 dolls.

16. $3 \times 12 = 36$

$\quad 3 \times 20 = 60$

$\quad$ Total number of colored pencils = $36 + 60 = 96$

$\quad 96 \div 8 = 12$

$\quad$ There are 12 colored pencils in each packet.

Test Prep 4

1. A $\qquad$ 2. C $\qquad$ 3. C $\qquad$ 4. D

5. B

6. a. $5\frac{5}{8} \times 18 = \frac{45}{8} \times 18$

$\qquad\qquad\quad = \frac{810}{8}$

$\qquad\qquad\quad = \frac{808}{8} + \frac{2}{8}$

$\qquad\qquad\quad = 101 + \frac{2}{8}$

$\qquad\qquad\quad = 101\frac{2}{8} = 101\frac{1}{4}$

b. **Method 1**

$\frac{3}{8} \div 12 = \frac{3}{8} \div \frac{12}{1}$

$\qquad\quad = \frac{3}{8} \times \frac{1}{12}$

$\qquad\quad = \frac{3}{96}$

$\qquad\quad = \frac{1}{32}$

Method 2

$\frac{3}{8} \div 12 = \frac{1}{12}$ of $\frac{3}{8}$

$\qquad\quad = \frac{1}{12} \times \frac{3}{8}$

$\qquad\quad = \frac{3}{96}$

$\qquad\quad = \frac{1}{32}$

7.

$\frac{4}{5} \div 8 = \frac{4}{5} \times \frac{1}{8} = \frac{4}{40} = \frac{1}{10}$ m

Each piece is $\frac{1}{10}$ meter long.

8. $1\frac{3}{4} \times \$8 = \frac{7}{4} \times \$8 = \$14$

$\quad \$14 \times 10 = \$140$

$\quad$ He is paid $140 in 10 days.

9. $\frac{3}{4} \times \frac{1}{3} = \frac{1}{4}$

$\quad \frac{1}{4} \times 5 = \frac{5}{4} = 1\frac{1}{4}$

$\quad$ His brother will take $1\frac{1}{4}$ hours to paint 5 similar walls.

10. $\$80 \times \frac{3}{5} = \$48$

$\quad \$80 - \$48 = \$32$

$\quad \$32 \div 5 = \$6.40$

$\quad$ She spends $6.40 each day.

11.

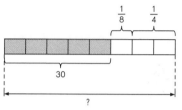

pink | blue | yellow

$1 - \dfrac{1}{4} = \dfrac{3}{4}$

$\dfrac{2}{3} \times \dfrac{3}{4} = \dfrac{1}{2}$

$\dfrac{1}{2}$ of the clips are yellow.

12.

$1 - \dfrac{1}{8} - \dfrac{1}{4} = \dfrac{5}{8}$

5 units → 30

1 unit → 6

8 units → 6 × 8 = 48

There are 48 pages in the book.

Benchmark Assessment 1 for Chapters 1 to 4

1. B   2. D
3. B   4. C
5. A   6. D
7. A   8. A
9. C   10. B

11. 700,000

12. 124,678

13. 657 ÷ 3 = 219
219 × \$4 = \$876
Billy must pay \$876 for all the mugs.

14. 15 × 32 = 480
480 ÷ 16 = 30
There are 30 people in each group.

15. $3\dfrac{2}{5} + 9\dfrac{4}{15} = 3\dfrac{6}{15} + 9\dfrac{4}{15}$

$= 12\dfrac{10}{15}$

$= 12\dfrac{2}{3}$

$\dfrac{2}{5} \xrightarrow{\times 3} = \xleftarrow{\times 3} \dfrac{6}{15}$

16. $\dfrac{6}{25} \times \dfrac{3}{4} = \dfrac{6 \times 3}{25 \times 4}$

$= \dfrac{18}{100}$

$= 0.18$

17.

36

$\dfrac{1}{3}$

$\dfrac{3}{5}$

4 units → 36
1 unit → 9
5 units → 5 × 9 = 45
Belinda uses 45 beads to make the bracelet.

18. $1\dfrac{2}{3} + 2\dfrac{1}{2} = 1\dfrac{4}{6} + 2\dfrac{3}{6}$

$= 3\dfrac{7}{6}$

$= 3 + \dfrac{7}{6}$

$= 3 + 1\dfrac{1}{6}$

$= 4\dfrac{1}{6}$

She baked $4\dfrac{1}{6}$ pounds of biscuits in all.

19. Width: $\dfrac{1}{4} \times \dfrac{2}{5} = \dfrac{1}{10}$ m

Perimeter $= 2 \times (\dfrac{2}{5} + \dfrac{1}{10}) = 1$ m

The perimeter of the rectangle is 1 meter.

20.
$$\begin{array}{r} 16 \\ 8\overline{)132} \\ \underline{80} \\ 52 \\ \underline{48} \\ 4 \end{array}$$

132 ÷ 8 = 16 R 4
The travel company needs to book 17 boats.

21. $1\dfrac{1}{2} \times \dfrac{2}{3} + 3\dfrac{3}{5} \times \dfrac{5}{6}$

$= \dfrac{3}{2} \times \dfrac{2}{3} + \dfrac{18}{5} \times \dfrac{5}{6}$

$= 1 + 3$

$= 4$ L

Patrick has 4 liters of purple paint.

22.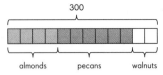

| | | | | |
|almonds|pecans|walnuts| | |

12 units → 300
1 unit → 25
2 units → 50
There are 50 walnuts in the bag.

23. $5,170 + $450 + $626 = $6,246
$6,246 ÷ 2 = $3,123
Mrs. Jefferson had $3,123 − $626 = $2,497.
Mr. Jefferson had $3,123 − $450 = $2,673.

Bonus Questions

1. Strategies: Make a systematic list. Guess and check.

10 Gift Cards		Total Number of Sides	Check
Number of Triangles	Number of Squares		
$2 \times 3 = 6$	$8 \times 4 = 32$	38	✗
$3 \times 3 = 9$	$7 \times 4 = 28$	37	✗
$4 \times 3 = 12$	$6 \times 4 = 24$	36	✗
$5 \times 3 = 15$	$5 \times 4 = 20$	35	✗
$6 \times 3 = 18$	$4 \times 4 = 16$	34	✔

Leslie has 4 square cards.

2. Strategy: Make a systematic list.

	Number of Eggs					
Groups of 4 eggs + 3	7	11	15	19	23	㉗
Groups of 5 eggs + 2	7	12	17	22	㉗	
Groups of 9 eggs	9	18	㉗			

The least number of eggs the grocer had is 27 eggs.

Pre-Test 5

1. inverse operations
2. equal; greater than; less than
3. order of operations
4. <   5. =
6. <   7. >
8. 9   9. 32, 32
10. 12   11. 76
12. 140   13. 24

14. $2 + (7 − 4) \times 3 = 2 + 3 \times 3$
$= 2 + 9$
$= 11$

15. $(95 − 15) ÷ 10 = 8$
He needs 8 plastic bags.

Test Prep 5

1. B   2. C   3. A   4. D
5. D
6. $3 + x − 100$
7. $60 − y$ or $(60 − y)$

8. a. $17y + 8$ b. $\dfrac{z − 24}{8} + 2$

9. a. $4x + 3$ $\dfrac{100x}{20} = \dfrac{100 \times 9}{20}$

   $= (4 \times 9) + 3$ $= \dfrac{900}{20}$

   $= 36 + 3$ $= 45$

   $= 39$

   $4x + 3 \; \boxed{<} \; \dfrac{100x}{20}$

   b. $(100 − 2x) ÷ 2$ $4 \times (x + 1)$
   $= (100 − 2 \times 9) ÷ 2$ $= 4 \times (9 + 1)$
   $= (100 ÷ 18) ÷ 2$ $= 4 \times 10$
   $= 82 ÷ 2$ $= 40$
   $= 41$
   $(100 − 2x) ÷ 2 \; \boxed{>} \; 4 \times (x + 1)$

10. a. $18m − 52 = 5m$
    $18m − 52 + 52 = 5m + 52$
    $18m = 5m + 52$
    $18m − 5m = 5m + 52 − 5m$
    $13m = 52$
    $13m ÷ 13 = 52 ÷ 13$
    $m = 4$

    b. $4p + 8 = 12p − 16$
    $4p + 8 + 16 = 12p − 16 + 16$
    $4p + 24 = 12p$
    $4p + 24 − 4p = 12p − 4p$
    $24 = 8p$
    $8p = 24$
    $8p ÷ 8 = 24 ÷ 8$
    $p = 3$

11. a. $3 \times p = 3p$
    $3p + 2$
    Cheryl has $3p + 2$ oranges.
    b. $3p + 2 = 3 \times 6 + 2$
    $= 20$
    Cheryl has 20 oranges.

12. a. If $y = 3$,

Ernie → $3y + 4 = 3 \times 3 + 4 = 13$

Gladice → $4y - 5 = 4 \times 3 - 5 = 7$

Ernie read more books.

b. $3y + 4 = 4y - 5$

$3y + 4 + 5 = 4y - 5 + 5$

$3y + 9 = 4y$

$3y + 9 - 3y = 4y - 3y$

$9 = y$

$y = 9$

When $y = 9$, both of them will read the same number of books.

1. area
2. square units
3. triangles
4. formula
5.

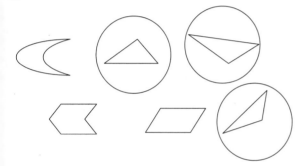

6. a. obtuse angle
   b. right angle
   c. acute angle
7. b
8.

9. 48 cm²
10. 12 in.²
11. 175 ft²
12. 81 yd²
13. 680 m²
14. $3 \text{ m} \times 2 \text{ m} = 6 \text{ m}^2$

The garden's area is 6 square meters.
15. Area of land = $50 \times 50 = 2{,}500 \text{ m}^2$

Area of land and footpath = 56×56

$= 3{,}136 \text{ m}^2$

Area of footpath = $3{,}136 - 2{,}500 = 636 \text{ m}^2$

The area of the footpath is 636 square meters.

1. B
2. D
3. A
4. C
5. B

6.

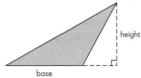

7. Base: $\overline{DC}$

Height: $\overline{BD}$

8. Area of triangle $CDE = \frac{1}{2} \times$ base $\times$ height

$= \frac{1}{2} \times 24 \text{ m} \times 24 \text{ m}$

$= 288 \text{ m}^2$

9. Area of the shaded triangle

$= \frac{1}{2} \times$ base $\times$ height

$= \frac{1}{2} \times 20 \text{ cm} \times 5 \text{ cm}$

$= 50 \text{ cm}^2$

10. Area of the rectangle = $15 \text{ in.} \times 20 \text{ in.}$

$= 300 \text{ in.}^2$

Area of the 2 triangles

$= \frac{1}{2} \times 8 \text{ in.} \times 15 \text{ in.} + \frac{1}{2} \times 6 \text{ in.} \times 15 \text{ in.}$

$= 60 \text{ in.}^2 + 45 \text{ in.}^2$

$= 105 \text{ in.}^2$

Area of the shaded part = $300 \text{ in.}^2 - 105 \text{ in.}^2$

$= 195 \text{ in.}^2$

11. Area of the rectangle = $8 \text{ cm} \times 9 \text{ cm} = 72 \text{ cm}^2$

Area of the unshaded triangle

$= \frac{1}{2} \times 8 \text{ cm} \times 9 \text{ cm} = 36 \text{ cm}^2$

Area of the shaded part of the figure

$= 72 \text{ cm}^2 - 36 \text{ cm}^2$

$= 36 \text{ cm}^2$

12. Length of the rectangle = $(60 - 24) \div 2$

$= 18 \text{ m}$

Area of the rectangle = $18 \times 12 = 216 \text{ m}^2$

Area of the shaded part of the figure

$= 216 - (\frac{1}{2} \times 18 \times 8) - (\frac{1}{2} \times 12 \times 4)$

$= 120 \text{ m}^2$

1. numerator; denominator
2. bar model
3.

16 — 9 — 7

4.

25 — 18 — 7

5. 2 out of 7 parts
6. 8 out of 9 parts

7. $\dfrac{9}{12} = \dfrac{3}{4}$ 8. $\dfrac{24}{60} = \dfrac{2}{5}$

9. From the model,

5 parts → 30

1 part → 6

8 parts → 8 × 6 = 48

3 parts → 3 × 6 = 18

A = 48; B = 18

10.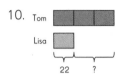

22 × 2 = 44

Tom has 44 more stamps than Lisa.

Test Prep 7

1. A 2. C 3. B 4. D

5. C

6. Number of black beads = 7 + 12 + 9

= 28

Number of white beads = 9 + 3 + 4

= 16

$\dfrac{28}{16} = \dfrac{7}{4}$

The number of black beads is $\dfrac{7}{4}$ times the number of white beads.

7. $5 : \boxed{4} : 9 = \boxed{15} : 12 : 27$

8.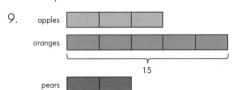

The ratio of the time Ron spends reading to the time he spends on the computer to the total time he spends on both activities is 1 : 2 : 3.

9.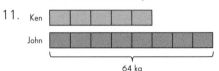

5 units → 15

1 unit → 15 ÷ 5 = 3

Total number of units = 3 + 5 + 2 = 10

10 × 3 = 30

There are 30 fruits in all.

10.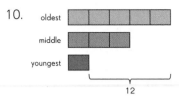

4 units → 12 years

3 units → (12 ÷ 4) × 3 = 9 years

The middle child is 9 years old.

11.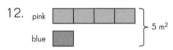

a. 5 : 8

b. 8 units → 64 kg

3 units → (64 ÷ 8) × 3 = 24 kg

John is 24 kilograms heavier than Ken.

12.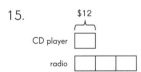

a. 1 : 4

b. 5 units → 5 m²

4 units → (5 ÷ 5) × 4 = 4 m²

The area of the part of the door that is painted pink is 4 square meters.

Mid-Year Test

1. C 2. C 3. A 4. A

5. B 6. D 7. C 8. B

9. D 10. B

11. 4,192,560

12. 6,315 → 6,000

72 → 70

6,000 × 70 = (6,000 × 7) × 10

= 420,000

13. 32 + (25 ÷ 5) − 21 ÷ 7 = 32 + 5 − 21 ÷ 7

= 32 + 5 − 3

= 34

14. $\dfrac{4}{5} ÷ 20 = \dfrac{4}{5} × \dfrac{1}{20} = \dfrac{4}{100} = 0.04$

15.

1 unit → $12

3 units → 3 × $12 = $36

The radio costs $36.

16. $2\frac{3}{4} - \frac{1}{5} = 2\frac{15}{20} - \frac{4}{20} = 2\frac{11}{20}$

$2\frac{3}{4} + 2\frac{11}{20} = 2\frac{15}{20} + 2\frac{11}{20}$

$= 4\frac{26}{20}$

$= 5\frac{6}{20} = 5\frac{3}{10}$

It takes $5\frac{3}{10}$ hours to complete both projects.

17. Area of the rectangle $= 10$ cm $\times 24$ cm
$= 240$ cm^2

Area of the unshaded parts
$= 2 \times (\frac{1}{2} \times 5$ cm $\times 12$ cm$) = 60$ cm^2

Area of the shaded part $= 240$ cm$^2 - 60$ cm^2
$= 180$ cm^2

18. Pens $\longrightarrow x$
Rulers $\longrightarrow 5 \times x = 5x$
Pencils $\longrightarrow x - 3$
$x + 5x + (x - 3) = 7x - 3$

They sold a total of $7x - 3$ items at the carnival.

19. Sandy's age : Tammy's age $= 1 : 4$
Jim's age : Tammy's age $= 2 : 1 = 8 : 4$
Jim's age : Tammy's age : Sandy's age $= 8 : 4 : 1$

The ratio of Jim's age to Tammy's age to Sandy's age is $8 : 4 : 1$.

20. Area of triangle $PQR = \frac{1}{2} \times 15$ in. $\times 36$ in.
$= 270$ in.^{2}

Area of triangle $QRS = \frac{1}{2} \times 15$ in. $\times 16$ in.
$= 120$ in.^{2}

Area of the shaded part $= 270$ in.$^2 - 120$ in.^{2}
$= 150$ in.^{2}

21.

Quarter	Dime	Total Amount	Check ($22.40)
10	3	$2.50 + $0.30 = $2.80	✗
60	18	$15 + $1.80 = $16.80	✗
70	21	$17.50 + $2.10 = $19.60	✗
80	24	$20 + $2.40 = $22.40	✔

There are 80 quarters and 24 dimes.

22. 2 boxes of crayons $\longrightarrow$ $18 - $10 = $8
1 box of crayons $\longrightarrow$ $8 ÷ 2 = $4
3 erasers $\longrightarrow$ $10 - $4 = $6
1 eraser $\longrightarrow$ $6 ÷ 3 = $2
1 box of crayons and 1 eraser $\longrightarrow$ $4 + $2 = $6
1 box of crayons and 1 eraser cost $6.

23. $\frac{2}{5}$ of the books are fiction books.

So, $1 - \frac{2}{5} = \frac{3}{5}$ of the books are non-fiction books.

Total number of fiction mystery books
$= \frac{2}{5} \times \frac{1}{5} = \frac{2}{25}$

Total number of non-fiction mystery books
$= \frac{3}{5} \times \frac{1}{3} = \frac{1}{5}$

$\frac{2}{25} + \frac{1}{5} = \frac{7}{25}$

$\frac{7}{25}$ of all the books in the shop are mystery books.

Bonus Questions

1. Strategy: Simplify the problem.
Area of the whole figure $= 15 \times 15$
$= 225$ cm^2
Area of the shaded part $= 5 \times 5$
$= 25$ cm^2
Area of the unshaded part $= 225 - 25$
$= 200$ cm^2

The area of the unshaded part of the figure is 200 square centimeters.

2. Strategy: Draw a diagram.

Distance between each tree $= \frac{3}{5} ÷ 3 = \frac{1}{5}$ m

Distance between 1st and 10th tree $= \frac{1}{5} \times 9$
$= \frac{9}{5}$
$= 1\frac{4}{5}$ m

The distance between the 1st tree and the 10th tree is $1\frac{4}{5}$ meters.

Pre-Test 8

1. tenths
2. hundredths
3. nearest whole number
4. nearest tenth
5. decimals

6. a. 1.7   b. 10.18
7. a. 1.6   b. 3.28
8. 4.13   9.   9.2

10. $\frac{3}{20} = \frac{15}{100} = 0.15$

$$\frac{3}{20} = \frac{15}{100}$$

$$\frac{17}{50} = \frac{34}{100}$$

11. $3\frac{17}{50} = 3 + \frac{17}{50}$

$$= 3 + \frac{34}{100}$$

$$= 3 + 0.34 = 3.34$$

12. 3; 2.7   13. 5; 5.2
14. 10; 9.6   15. 1; 1.0
16. 8; 7.9   17. 3; 3.0

18. $1\frac{2}{5} - \frac{17}{20} = \frac{7}{5} - \frac{17}{20} = \frac{28}{20} - \frac{17}{20}$

$$= \frac{11}{20}$$

$$\frac{11}{20} = \frac{11 \times 5}{20 \times 5} = \frac{55}{100} = 0.55 \text{ m}$$

0.55 m is about 0.6 m.
The length of the remaining piece of ribbon is about 0.6 m.

Test Prep 8

1. B   2. C   3. D   4. A
5. B
6.

```
0.00      0.01      0.02      0.03      0.04
```

7. a. $5\frac{18}{1000}$
        = 5 ones and 1 hundredth 8 thousandths
        = 5.018
    b. $2\frac{349}{1000}$
        = 2 ones and 3 tenths 4 hundredths
          9 thousandths
        = 2.349

8. 3.178   3.6   6.63   10.1
9. 8.275 = 8 + 0.2 + 0.07 + 0.005
10. 1.650 rounded to the nearest tenth is 1.7.
    1.649 rounded to the nearest tenth is 1.6.
    So, the greatest possible decimal is 1.649.
11. 850 mL = $\frac{850}{1000}$ L = 0.85 L
    1,200 mL = 1.2 L
    1.2 L + 0.85 L = 2.05 L
    She makes 2.05 liters of fruit punch.

12. 6.149 rounded to the nearest tenth is 6.1.
    6.150 rounded to the nearest tenth is 6.2.
    So, the shortest possible height of the vase is 6.150 feet.

Pre-Test 9

1. multiplied by 10   2.   divided by 1,000
3. estimation   4.   370
5. 13,600   6.   85,000
7. 92 × 30 = 92 × (3 × 10)
            = (92 × 3) × 10
            = 276 × 10
            = 2,760
8. 381 × 500 = 381 × (5 × 100)
             = (381 × 5) × 100
             = 1,905 × 100
             = 190,500
9. 76 × 8,000 = 76 × (8 × 1,000)
              = (76 × 8) × 1,000
              = 608,000
10. 640
11. 39
12. 8
13. 540 ÷ 90 = (540 ÷ 9) ÷ 10
            = 60 ÷ 10
            = 6
14. 6,300 ÷ 700 = (6,300 ÷ 7) ÷ 100
              = 900 ÷ 100
              = 9
15. 72,000 ÷ 8,000 = (72,000 ÷ 8) ÷ 1,000
                 = 9,000 ÷ 1,000
                 = 9
16. 623 rounds to 600.
    59 rounds to 60.
    600 × 60 = (600 × 6) × 10
            = 3,600 × 10
            = 36,000
    623 × 59 is about 36,000.
17. 9,842 rounds to 9,800.
    36 rounds to 40.
    9,800 ÷ 40 = (9,800 ÷ 4) ÷ 10
              = 2,450 ÷ 10
              = 245
    9,842 ÷ 36 is about 245.

18.

$7.65

buttons ▭ $16.25

fabric ▭▭

a. $7.65 + $16.25 = $23.90
   Suzanne paid $23.90 for the items.
b. $50 − $23.90 = $26.10
   She got $26.10 in change.

19. a. 208 × 50 = 208 × (5 × 10)
       = (208 × 5) × 10
       = 1,040 × 10
       = 10,400
   There are 10,400 roses in all.
   b. 10,400 ÷ 20 = (10,400 ÷ 2) ÷ 10
       = 5,200 ÷ 10
       = 520
   He needs 520 boxes

1. B
2. C
3. A
4. D
5. C
6. a. 1,000   b. 100
7.
     $\overset{5\ 2}{6.8\,4}$
   $\times\qquad\quad 7$
   $\overline{4\,7.8\,8}$

8. a. 23.63 rounds to 24.
      15.3 rounds to 15.
      24 + 15 = 39
      23.63 + 15.3 is about 39.
   b. 17.85 rounds to 18.
      9.49 rounds to 9.
      18 − 9 = 9
      17.85 − 9.49 is about 9.

9. 5 m ÷ 8 = 0.625 m
   0.625 rounded to the nearest hundredth is 0.63.
   Each piece of rope is about 0.63 meter long.

10. 1.065 lb × 8 = 8.52 lb
    15 lb − 8.52 lb = 6.48 lb
    6.48 pounds of flour is left after 8 days.

11. Cost of 2 pounds of grapes = 2 × $2.49
                               = $4.98
    Cost of 3 muffins = 3 × $0.75 = $2.25
    $4.98 + $2.25 = $7.23
    He paid $7.23 for the grapes and muffins.

12.

$90

$20 ┊ ┊ ┊ $20

? ($20 bills)

$27.90 is about $30.
3 × $30 = $90
The total cost of 3 chairs is about $90.
$90 ÷ $20 = 4.5
He needs at least 5 $20 bills to buy the chairs.

1. out of   2. decimal
3. fraction   4. equivalent; denominator
5. 0.28   6. 0.73
7. $\dfrac{19}{100}$ 8. $\dfrac{91}{100}$
9. 3; 40   10. 79; 100
11. 58; 100   12. 32; 100

13. $\dfrac{9}{12} = \dfrac{3}{\boxed{4}} = \dfrac{\boxed{75}}{100}$

14. $\dfrac{4}{\boxed{7}} = \dfrac{16}{\boxed{28}} = \dfrac{28}{49}$

15. $\dfrac{2}{5} = \dfrac{4}{\boxed{10}} = \dfrac{18}{\boxed{45}}$

16. $\dfrac{9}{25} = \dfrac{18}{\boxed{50}} = \dfrac{\boxed{36}}{100}$

17. $\dfrac{14}{25}$ 18. $\dfrac{3}{4}$

19. $\dfrac{1}{2}$ 20. $\dfrac{4}{5}$

21.

22. 300 g = $\dfrac{300}{1000}$ = 0.3 kg
    1.4 kg + 0.3 kg = 1.7 kg
    The mass of the mixture is 1.7 kilograms.

23. 2.4 − (1.75 + 0.2) = 0.45 L
    0.45 L = $\dfrac{45}{100}$ L = $\dfrac{9}{20}$ L
    $\dfrac{9}{20}$ liter of lemonade is left.

1. D 2. A 3. C 4. B
5. D

6. $45\% = \dfrac{45}{100} = \dfrac{45 \div 5}{100 \div 5} = \dfrac{9}{20}$

7. Total number of people = 200
   Number of women = 200 − 80 = 120
   $\dfrac{120}{200} = \dfrac{60}{100} = 60\%$
   60% of the people are women.

8. Total number of students = 680
   Number of girls = 55% × 680
   $\qquad\qquad\quad = \dfrac{55}{100} \times 680$
   $\qquad\qquad\quad = 374$
   Number of boys = 680 − 374 = 306
   374 − 306 = 68
   There are 68 more girls than boys.

9. 100% − 75% − 12% = 13%
   13% are green beads.
   13% → 104 beads
   1% → 104 ÷ 13 = 8 beads
   12% → 12 × 8 = 96 beads
   Lucy has 96 blue beads.

10. 100% → $3,500
    1% → $3,500 ÷ 100 = $35
    72% → $35 × 72 = $2,520
    He spends $2,520.
    $3,500 − $2,520 = $980
    25% of $980 = $245
    He saves $245.
    $980 − $245 = $735
    Mr. Daniels' rent is $735.

11.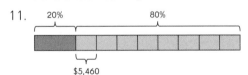

    $5,460 × 8 = $43,680
    80% → $43,680
    1% → $\dfrac{\$43,680}{80} = \$546$
    20% → $546 × 20 = $10,920
    Cost of the car = $43,680 + $10,920
    $\qquad\qquad\qquad = $54,600
    The car costs $54,600.

12.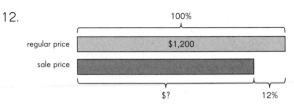

a. **Method 1**
   100% → $1,200
   1% → $1,200 ÷ 100 = $12
   12% → 12 × $12 = $144
   The dollar amount of the discount was $144.

   Method 2
   Discount = 12% of regular price
   $\qquad\quad = \dfrac{12}{100} \times \$1,200$
   $\qquad\quad = \$144$

b. $1,200 − $144 = $1,056
   The airline ticket cost $1,056.

   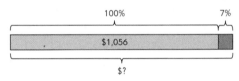

   100% → $1,056
   1% → $1,056 ÷ 100 = $10.56
   7% → 7 × $10.56 = $73.92
   $1,056 + $73.92 = $1,129.92
   Mr. Sims paid $1,129.92.

Benchmark Assessment 2 for Chapters 8 to 10

1. B 2. C 3. B 4. C
5. A 6. A 7. D 8. C
9. D 10. B

11. 3 tens and 25 thousandths = 30.025

12. $\dfrac{9675}{1000} = 9.675$

    9.675 is nearer to 10 than to 9.
    So, 9.675 rounds to 10.

13. $7.065 = 7\dfrac{65}{1000} = 7\dfrac{13}{200}$

14. 900 × 3.168
    = (100 × 9) × 3.168
    = 100 × (9 × 3.168)
    = 100 × 28.512
    = 2,851.2

    $$\begin{array}{r} \overset{\scriptstyle 1\ \ \, 6\ 7}{3.168} \\ \times \qquad 9 \\ \hline 28.512 \end{array}$$

15. 6.24 ÷ 10 = 0.624
    624 ÷ 1,000 = 0.624
    So, 6.24 ÷ 10 = <u>624</u> ÷ 1,000

16. 8.75 pounds rounds to 9 pounds.
    36 rounds to 40.
    Weight of 1 chicken drumstick
    $= 9 \text{ lb} \div 40$
    $= \dfrac{9}{40}$
    $= \dfrac{9 \times 25}{40 \times 25}$
    $= \dfrac{225}{1000}$
    $= 0.225 \text{ lb}$
    Each chicken drumstick weighs about
    0.225 pound.

17. Number of non-school holidays in April
    $= 30 - 6 = 24$
    $\dfrac{24}{30} \times 100\% = 80\%$

    80% of the days in April are not school holidays.

18. 15% of $360 = \dfrac{15}{100} \times \$360 = \$54$

    18% of $720 = \dfrac{18}{100} \times \$720 = \$129.60$

    Difference $= \$129.60 - \$54 = \$75.60$

19.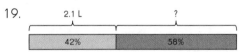

    $42\% \rightarrow 2.1 \text{ L}$
    $1\% \rightarrow 2.1 \div 42 = 0.05 \text{ L}$
    $58\% \rightarrow 58 \times 0.05 = 2.9 \text{ L}$
    Leon used 2.9 liters of brown paint.

20.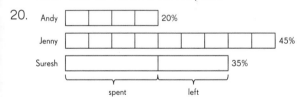

    $\dfrac{3}{5} \times 35\% = \dfrac{3}{5} \times \dfrac{35}{100} = \dfrac{105}{500} = \dfrac{21}{100} = 21\%$

    Suresh spends 21% of the total amount of money.
    $35\% - 21\% = 14\%$
    Suresh has 14% of the total amount of money left.

21.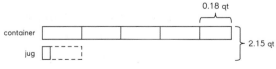

    5 parts $\rightarrow$ 2.15 qt
    1 part $\rightarrow$ 2.15 ÷ 5 = 0.43 qt
    4 parts $\rightarrow$ 4 × 0.43 = 1.72 qt
    1.72 qt + 0.18 qt = 1.9 qt
    There were 1.9 quarts of oil in the container at first.

22.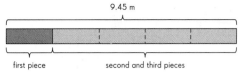

    5 units $\rightarrow$ 9.45 m
    1 unit $\rightarrow$ 1.89 m
    4 units $\rightarrow$ 7.56 m
    The second and third pieces of rope were
    7.56 meters long.

    7.56 m $-$ 0.12 m $=$ 7.44 m
    2 units $\rightarrow$ 7.44 m
    1 unit $\rightarrow$ 3.72 m
    3.72 m $+$ 0.12 m $=$ 3.84 m
    The second piece of rope was 3.84 meters long.

23. a.

    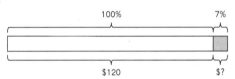

    100% $\rightarrow$ $120
      1% $\rightarrow$ $120 ÷ 100 = $1.20
      7% $\rightarrow$ 7 × $1.20 = $8.40
    The tax was $8.40.
    b. 15% $\rightarrow$ 15 × $1.20 = $18
    The tip was $18.
    c. Total cost of the meal
    $= \$120 + \$8.40 + \$18$
    $= \$146.40$
    $\$146.40 ÷ 5 = \$29.28$
    Each of them had to pay $29.28.

Bonus Questions

1. Strategy: Make logical deduction.
    Volume of 9 bottles = Volume of 12 pails
    Divide both sides by 3:
    Volume of 3 bottles = Volume of 4 pails
    Volume of 3 bottles and 5 pails
    = Volume of 4 pails + Volume of 5 pails
    21.6 L = Volume of 9 pails
    Volume of 9 pails = 21.6 L
    Volume of 1 pail = 21.6 ÷ 9
                     = 2.4 L
    The volume of 1 pail is 2.4 liters.

2. Strategy: Draw a model.

$100\% - (50\% + 40\%) = 10\%$
$10\% \longrightarrow 6$ min.
$100\% \longrightarrow 6 \times 10 = 60$ min.
60 min. $\div 5 = 12$ min.
Pauline should have spent 12 minutes on each question.

Pre-Test 11

1. mean
2. table; tally chart
3. graph
4. probability
5. more likely
6. impossible
7. a.

Cookies Sold in a Week

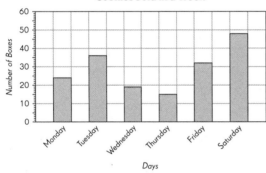

Days

b. Saturday

8. 1.2 kg $= 1,200$ g
Total mass of the 4 objects
$= 45$ g $+ 76$ g $+ 103$ g $+ 1,200$ g
$= 1,424$ g
Average mass $= 1,424$ g $\div 4 = 356$ g

9. a. less likely
   b. impossible
   c. certain
   d. less likely

10. a. $\dfrac{\boxed{1}}{\boxed{6}}$

    b. $\dfrac{2}{6} = \dfrac{\boxed{1}}{\boxed{3}}$

    c. $\dfrac{3}{6} = \dfrac{\boxed{1}}{\boxed{2}}$

11. a. 19 quarters
    b. $24 - 15 = 9$
       He saved 9 more quarters in Week 2 than in Week 1.
    c. $15 + 24 + 19 + 30 = 88$
       He saved 88 quarters in 4 weeks.
    d. $88 \times 25¢ = 88 \times \$0.25 = \$22$
       Bob saved \$22.
    e. $\$22 \div 4 = \$5.50$
       He saved an average of \$5.50 per week.

12. Total amount of water in the 5 containers
    $=$ mean amount of water $\times$ number of containers
    $= 620$ mL $\times 5$
    $= 3,100$ mL
    Amount of water in the fifth container
    $= 3,100$ mL $- 2,750$ mL
    $= 350$ mL
    The amount of water in the fifth container is 350 mL.

Test Prep 11

1. C   2. C   3. A   4. D
5. B
6. a. George: $\$32 + \$25 + \$40 = \$97$
      Henry: $\$36 + \$34 + \$29 = \$99$
      Henry made more money.
   b. $\$99 - \$97 = \$2$
      He made \$2 more.

7.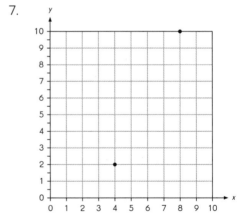

8. 7 meters

9.

Flavors	Toppings	Combinations
strawberry	peanuts	strawberry, peanuts
	raisins	strawberry, raisins
chocolate	peanuts	chocolate, peanuts
	raisins	chocolate, raisins
vanilla	peanuts	vanilla, peanuts
	raisins	vanilla, raisins

ice cream

The shop can offer $3 \times 2 = 6$ combinations.

10. a. Number of times a black ball is drawn
$$= 50 - 15 - 26 = 9$$
Experimental probability $= \dfrac{9}{50}$

b. Theoretical probability $= \dfrac{3}{5 + 3 + 4} = \dfrac{3}{12}$
$$= \dfrac{1}{4}$$

Experimental probability $= \dfrac{26}{50}$

$$\dfrac{26}{50} - \dfrac{1}{4} = \dfrac{52}{100} - \dfrac{25}{100} = \dfrac{27}{100}$$

The difference between the theoretical probability and the experimental probability of getting a green ball is $\dfrac{27}{100}$.

11. From the graph,
45 ft → 15 yd
72 ft → 24 yd
Area of land = 15 yd × 24 yd = 360 yd^2
The area of the rectangular plot of land is 360 square yards.

12. a.

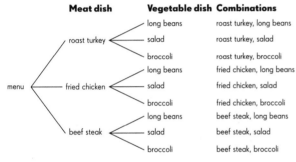

Meat dish	Vegetable dish	Combinations
roast turkey	long beans	roast turkey, long beans
	salad	roast turkey, salad
	broccoli	roast turkey, broccoli
fried chicken	long beans	fried chicken, long beans
	salad	fried chicken, salad
	broccoli	fried chicken, broccoli
beef steak	long beans	beef steak, long beans
	salad	beef steak, salad
	broccoli	beef steak, broccoli

She can choose from 3 × 3 = 9 combinations.
b. Ms. Spencer can choose from 4 × 3 = 12 combinations.

Pre-Test 12

1. line; points
2. line segment
3. rays; angle
4. perpendicular lines
5. right angle
6. points; line
7. line segment; ray
8. $\overline{EF}$ and $\overline{CD}$
9. a. 4   b. 360°
10.
11. ∠TUV or ∠VUT   12. ∠BOC or ∠COB
13. 65°   14. 125°
15. Measure of ∠x = 90° − 12° = 78°
16. Measure of ∠y = 45° − 18° = 27°

Test Prep 12

1. A   2. B   3. C   4. D
5. C
6. 86° + x + x = 180°
   x + x = 180° − 86°
   2x = 94°
   x = 94° ÷ 2 = 47°
7. m∠p + 63° + 90° + 78° = 360°
   m∠p + 231° = 360°
   m∠p = 360° − 231°
   = 129°
8. m∠a + 90° = 137°
   m∠a = 137° − 90° = 47°
9. m∠ABC = 90°
   m∠EBF = m∠ABD = 90° − 45° = 45°
   The measure of ∠EBF is 45°.
10. m∠p + 90° + 90° + 125° = 360°
    m∠p + 305° = 360°
    m∠p = 360° − 305°
    = 55°
11. m∠p + 71° + 90° + m∠q + 90° + m∠r
    = 360°
    m∠p + m∠q + m∠r = 360° − 251°
    = 109°
12. m∠DBH = 180° − 90° = 90°
    m∠CBD = 90° − 45° = 45°
    m∠CBH = 90° − 45° = 45°
    m∠CBG = m∠CBH ÷ 2 = 45° ÷ 2
    = 22.5°
    m∠DBG = 45° + 22.5° = 67.5°
    m∠FBE = m∠DBG = 67.5°

Pre-Test 13

1. polygon   2. vertices
3. triangles   4. quadrilaterals
5. trapezoid   6. inequality
7. a. rectangle   b. parallelogram   c. rhombus
   d. square   e. triangle   f. trapezoid
8. three   9. equal
10. parallel   11. opposite
12. one
13. greater than; less than
14. a. m∠ _q_ + m∠ _p_ = 180° or
    m∠ _q_ + m∠ _x_ ; m∠ _x_ + m∠ _DOB_ ;
    m∠ _p_ + m∠ _DOB_
    b. m∠x + m∠ _y_ + m∠ _z_ = 180°
    c. m∠p + m∠ _y_ + m∠ _z_ = 180°

15. <   16. =

17. >   18. rhombus

19. trapezoid

Test Prep 13

1. A   2. B   3. D   4. C

5. A

6. $m\angle ABC + m\angle BAC + m\angle ACB = 180°$
$52° + 65° + m\angle ACB = 180°$
$m\angle ACB = 180° - 52° - 65°$
$= 63°$
$m\angle BCD = 180° - 63° = 117°$
$m\angle a + 30° + m\angle BCD = 180°$
$m\angle a + 30° + 117° = 180°$
$m\angle a + 147° = 180°$
$m\angle a = 180° - 147°$
$= 33°$

7. a. $m\angle ACB = 180° - 69° - 90° = 21°$
$m\angle BAC \; \text{>} \; m\angle ACB$
b. $69° - 21° = 48°$
$m\angle BAC$ is greater than $m\angle ACB$ by $48°$.

8. $m\angle CED = 90° - 60° = 30°$
$m\angle a = m\angle CED = 30°$

9. $m\angle BCE = (180° - 56°) \div 2 = 62°$
$m\angle ABC = m\angle ADC = 84°$
$m\angle ABE = 62° + 84° = 146°$

10. $m\angle ABC = m\angle ADC = 76°$
$m\angle CAB = (180° - 76°) \div 2 = 52°$
$m\angle BAE = 180° - 52° = 128°$
$m\angle ABE = (180° - 128°) \div 2 = 26°$
$m\angle a = 360° - 26° - 76° = 258°$
$m\angle CAD = 52°$
$m\angle b = 180° - 52° = 128°$

11. $\angle 35° + \angle 73° + m\angle a + m\angle b + m\angle c + m\angle d = 180° + 180°$
$\angle 108° + m\angle a + m\angle b + m\angle c + m\angle d = 360°$
$m\angle a + m\angle b + m\angle c + m\angle d = 360° - 108° = 252°$
The sum of the measures of $\angle a, \angle b, \angle c,$ and $\angle d$ is $252°$.

12. $m\angle EDB = m\angle EAB = 110°$
$m\angle DBE = (180° - 110°) \div 2 = 70° \div 2 = 35°$
$m\angle BDC = 180° - 110° = 70°$
$m\angle CBD = 180° - 70° - 55° = 55°$
$m\angle EBC = 360° - 35° - 55° = 270°$
The measure of $\angle EBC$ is $270°$.

Pre-Test 14

1. plane figure   2. vertices

3. pentagon   4. pyramid

5. congruent

6. The plane figures are B, C, D, and F.
The solid figures are A and E.

7.
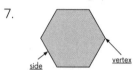

8. sphere   9. cone

10. cube, rectangular prism, or pyramid

11. $\overline{AB} \; // \; \overline{CD}$ or $\overline{AD} \; // \; \overline{BC}$

12. B and E, D and H, C and G

Test Prep 14

1. B   2. C   3. D   4. D

5. A

6. rectangular prism

7.
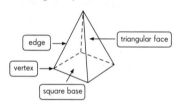

8. It does not have any flat, triangular faces.

9. a. 10 edges and 6 vertices
b. The base is a pentagon. The faces are triangles.

10.
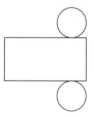

11. A and C

12. square pyramid

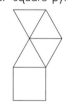

1. square
2. prism
3. triangular prism
4. volume
5. capacity
6. area, formulas
7. triangular prism
8. cube or square prism
9. rectangular prism
10. a. The volume of the juice in the jug is 3.5 quarts.
    b. The capacity of the jug is more than 5 quarts.
11. $\frac{2}{3} \times 30$ L $= 20$ L

    The volume of the water in the tank is 20 liters.
12. Area of the bathroom floor $= 2$ m $\times 2$ m $= 4$ m^2
    Area of the bedroom and study floor
    $= 8$ m $\times 2$ m
    $= 16$ m^2
    Area of the living room floor
    $= 6$ m $\times 3$ m
    $= 18$ m^2
    Total area $= 4$ m$^2 + 16$ m$^2 + 18$ m$^2 = 38$ m^2
    The total area of the floor of the apartment is 38 square meters.

Test Prep 15

1. C   2. C   3. B   4. D
5. B
6. 9 cubes are used to build the solid.
7.

8. Total surface area of the triangular prism
   $= 2 \times 15 \times 16 + 2 \times \frac{1}{2} \times 17 \times 12 +$
   17×16
   $= 956$ cm^2
9. Length $= 12 \times 2 = 24$ in.
   Volume of wood $= 12 \times 24 \times 8.5$
   $= 2,448$ in.^{3}
   The volume of the block of wood is 2,448 cubic inches.
10. Volume of water in the container
    $= 9 \times 12 \times 23 = 2,484$ cm$^3 = 2,484$ mL
    $2,484$ mL $\times \frac{2}{3} = 1,656$ mL
    $2,484$ mL $- 1,656$ mL $= 828$ mL
    She must pour out 828 milliliters of water from the container.

11. Capacity of the tank $= 320 \times 160 \times 200$
    $= 10,240,000$ cm^3
    Volume of water in the tank
    $= \frac{3}{4} \times 10,240,000$
    $= 7,680,000$ cm^3
    Capacity of a small container $= 16 \times 16 \times 5$
    $= 1,280$ cm^3
    Number of containers filled with water from the tank
    $= 7,680,000$ cm$^3 \div 1,280$ cm^3
    $= 6,000$
    The water from the tank can fill 6,000 small containers.
12. Capacity of the tank $= 30 \times 30 \times 50$
    $= 45,000$ cm$^3 = 45$ L
    $\frac{4}{5} \times 45$ L $= 36$ L
    The tank is filled with 36 liters of water.
    6 L $\longrightarrow$ 1 min
    36 L $\longrightarrow 36 \div 6 = 6$ min
    It will take 6 minutes to fill $\frac{4}{5}$ of the tank with water.

COMMON CORE — Focus Lessons Assessments

Chapter 2
1. 24,900
2. 185,000
3. 320,000
4. 5,700,000
5. 72
6. 48
7. 320
8. 324

Chapter 4
1. 56   2. 30   3. 63   4. 32
5. $5 \div \frac{1}{9} = 5 \times 9$
   $= 45$
   He can make 45 sandwiches with 5 cans of strawberry jam.
6. $6 \div \frac{1}{5} = 6 \times 5$
   $= 30$
   She can make 30 pies.
7. $9 - 5 = 4$ lb
   $4 \div \frac{1}{3} = 4 \times 3$
   $= 12$
   He puts sand into 12 fish tanks.

8. $7 - 3 = 4$ cups

$$4 \div \frac{1}{8} = 4 \times 8$$

$$= 32$$

She makes 32 blackberry tarts.

Chapter 6

1. $\frac{24}{49}$ ft²   2. $\frac{6}{25}$ yd²   3. $\frac{9}{32}$ ft²   4. $\frac{18}{25}$ in.²

Chapter 9

1. 39   2. 250.4   3. 1,826   4. 9,750

Chapter 11

1.

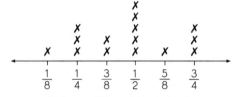

Volume of Water in Tanks (gal)
Key: Each ✗ stands for 1 tank.

2. 7 gal   3. $\frac{7}{15}$ gal

Chapter 15

1. 912 ft³   2. 459 m³
3. 2,272 in.³   4. 6,048 cm³
5. 740 cm³   6. 4,059 in.³
7. 5,040 in.³   8. 83,200 cm³

End-of-Year Test

1. B   2. D   3. C   4. B
5. A   6. C   7. A   8. D
9. B   10. C

11.
```
        7 6
        6 5
        6 8 7
  ×        9 8
  ─────────────
      5, 4 9 6
    6 1, 8 3 0
  ─────────────
    6 7, 3 2 6
```

12.
```
      1. 2 8 4
  5)6. 4 2
    5
    ─
    1 4
    1 0
    ───
      4 2
      4 0
      ───
        2 0
        2 0
        ───
          0
```

1.284 rounded to the nearest hundredth is 1.28.

13. $6\frac{1}{4} + 2\frac{7}{9} + 1\frac{3}{4} = 8 + 2\frac{7}{9} = 10\frac{7}{9}$

14. $5\frac{1}{2} \times 4 = \frac{11}{2} \times 4$

$$= \frac{11 \times 4}{2} = \frac{44}{2} = 22 \text{ lb}$$

The total weight of the charcoal is 22 pounds.

15. $14f + 2$

16.

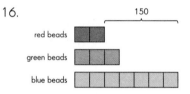

   5 parts ⟶ 150
    1 part ⟶ 150 ÷ 5 = 30
  12 parts ⟶ 12 × 30 = 360
There are 360 beads.

17. Number of combinations = 3 × 5 = 15
The teacher can choose from 15 combinations.

18. $m\angle ADC = 180° - 122° = 58°$
$m\angle ADE = 58° + 31° = 89°$
$m\angle DEA = (180° - 89°) \div 2 = 45.5°$

19. rectangular pyramid

20. Area covered by a face of solid B
    = 3 × 4 = 12 cm²
Surface area of solid A − 12 cm²
    = 2 × 10 × 9 + 2 × 10 × (7 + 4) +
      2 × 9 × (7 + 4) − 12 cm²
    = 586 cm²
The total surface area of solid A that is painted red is 586 square centimeters.

21. Amount of juice left $= 7\frac{2}{3} - \frac{5}{6}$

$\qquad\qquad\qquad = 6\frac{5}{6}$ pt

Amount of juice poured into 3 bottles

$= 6\frac{5}{6} \times \frac{3}{4} = 5\frac{1}{8}$ pt

Amount of juice in each bottle

$= 5\frac{1}{8} \div 3 = 1\frac{17}{24}$ pt

Each bottle contains $1\frac{17}{24}$ pints of pineapple juice.

22. Volume of water in the rectangular tank

$= 24 \times 12 \times 10 \times \frac{4}{5}$

$= 2{,}304$ cm$^3 = 2{,}304$ mL

Volume of water used to fill the cubical tank

$= 16 \times 16 \times 16 \times \frac{1}{2}$

$= 2{,}048$ cm$^3 = 2{,}048$ mL

Volume of water left in the rectangular tank

$= 2{,}304 - 2{,}048 = 256$ mL $= 0.256$ L

0.256 liter of water is left in the rectangular tank.

23. Number of buns baked $= 270 \div 3 = 90$

72% of baked products $\rightarrow 90 + 270 = 360$

 1% of baked products $\rightarrow 360 \div 72 = 5$

28% of baked products $\rightarrow 5 \times 28$

$\qquad\qquad\qquad\qquad\qquad = 140$ cookies

Number of buns left $= 90 - 40 = 50$

Number of cookies that should be left

$= 2 \times 50 = 100$

Number of cookies that need to be sold

$= 140 - 100 = 40$

The baker should sell 40 cookies so that the ratio of the number of buns left to the number of cakes left to the number of cookies left is 1 : 3 : 2.

Bonus Questions

1. Strategy: Make logical deduction.

    Cost of 5 erasers and 30 pencils
    $=$ Cost of 10 erasers and 24 pencils
    Subtract 5 erasers from each side:
    Cost of 30 pencils $=$ Cost of 5 erasers and
    $\qquad\qquad\qquad\qquad\qquad\qquad$ 24 pencils
    Subtract 24 pencils from each side:
    Cost of 6 pencils $=$ Cost of 5 erasers
    Cost of 5 erasers $= 5 \times \$0.30 = \$1.50$
    Cost of 1 pencil $= \dfrac{\$1.50}{6} = \$0.25$

    Each pencil costs $0.25.

2. Strategy: Simplify the problem.
    Area of each small triangle in figure 2
    $= 128$ cm$^2 \div 4 = 32$ cm^2
    Area of each smaller triangle in figure 3
    $= 32$ cm$^2 \div 4 = 8$ cm^2
    Area of each smallest triangle in figure 4
    $= 8$ cm$^2 \div 4 = 2$ cm^2
    The area of the smallest equilateral triangle in figure 4 is 2 square centimeters.

Student Record Sheet

Test	Date	Score	What I Need to Practice
Test Prep 1 Whole Numbers		25	
Test Prep 2 Whole Number Multiplication and Division		25	
Test Prep 3 Fractions and Mixed Numbers		25	
Test Prep 4 Multiplying and Dividing Fractions and Mixed Numbers		25	
Benchmark Assessment 1 for Chapters 1 to 4		50	
Test Prep 5 Algebra		25	
Test Prep 6 Area of a Triangle		25	
Test Prep 7 Ratio		25	
Mid-Year Test		50	

Name: _____

Student Record Sheet

Test	Date	Score	What I Need to Practice
Test Prep 8 Decimals		25	
Test Prep 9 Multiplying and Dividing Decimals		25	
Test Prep 10 Percent		25	
Benchmark Assessment 2 for Chapters 8 to 10		50	
Test Prep 11 Graphs and Probability		25	
Test Prep 12 Angles		25	
Test Prep 13 Properties of Triangles and Four-sided Figures		25	
Test Prep 14 Three-Dimensional Shapes		25	
Test Prep 15 Surface Area and Volume		25	
End-of-Year Test		50	

BLANK

BLANK

BLANK